HAUNTED BY
DICKENS

Humorous Asides and Personal
Insight into the Themes of
Charles Dickens'
A Christmas Carol

TIM LOWRY

ISBN: 979-8989306107

"A Christmas Carol"
Written by Charles Dickens
Illustrated by John Leech

Produced by Publish Pros | publishpros.com

DEDICATION

With gratitude to all my ghosts.

ACKNOWLEDGEMENTS

Sincerest appreciation to my contributors:
Deborah Westendorff, Cari Jarman, Lisa Marie Clancy,
Melissa McCrory, Wayne Lewis, Sarah Brady, Jennifer
Miller, Debbie Hopkins, Kat Mincz, Gregg Fuesel, Gina
Mays, Elizabeth Samples, Denice Fisher, Debra Wright,
Laura Deal, Nancy Puckett and Catherine Yael Serota.
Your support helped to make this book possible.

I would also like to thank my wife, Bonnie.

HAUNTED BY DICKENS

Humorous Asides and Personal
Insight into the Themes of
Charles Dickens'
A Christmas Carol

GHOSTS

Marley was dead: to begin with.

Any professional storyteller will tell you, Charles Dickens was on to something when he decided to write a ghost story. Of all the types of stories one might tell—personal narrative, fable, folktale, fairytale, historical story, wonder tale, parable, legend, epic, myth, you name it—the ghost story is definitely the most popular. In the opening paragraphs of *A Christmas Carol,* Dickens recognizes this fact by referencing the ghost of Hamlet's father, which was arguably England's most well-known literary ghost up to that point. However, one of Dickens' shortest works would eventually eclipse William Shakespeare's longest one, claiming the title of

England's most famous ghost story as it was read, re-read, dramatized, cinematized, televised, and monetized every year after its publication in 1843.

Twenty years ago, a brand new restaurant in Charleston, South Carolina wanted to put itself on the map with some special events to garner publicity. They hired me to be the "resident storyteller." Like a sommelier of stories, I would present particular tales to compliment the menu for a series of themed dinners. No matter what type of food the chef prepared, I quickly realized the audience always wanted a ghost story.

Previous to hiring me, the restaurant owners had seen the great-great-grandson of Charles Dickens, Mr. Gerald Dickens, perform *A Christmas Carol* when he was on tour in the United States. They had made an inquiry about booking Gerald for the restaurant, but when they found out what it would cost to bring the direct ancestor of Charles Dickens all the way from London, they called me instead. As Christmas approached, they asked if I might be able to perform *A Christmas Carol* in a dining room setting. The story of Ebenezer Scrooge and Tiny Tim had always been a personal favorite of mine, and taking the place of a direct ancestor of Mr. Dickens himself appealed to my ego. So, I got to work, learning the story from the same script Charles Dickens had used for his public readings when he toured the United States in 1867. It took about forty hours of rehearsal, but the effort was well worth it. The show was a hit. In fact, I have performed at the restaurant, Circa 1886, every year since. (Make your reservations now, because the show is always sold out months in advance!)

Whenever I tell any ghost story, and this most popular one in particular, the question is always asked, "Do you believe in ghosts?" Well, Charles Dickens certainly did. He makes that quite clear in his brief introduction. However, this ghost story is very different from anything ever told before. It is not merely a spooky story to entertain children. It is not one of those little anecdotes about a weird and unexplainable coincidence. And although it sounds like a traditional winter's tale from the British Dark Ages that might begin with "There was a man dwelt by a churchyard…," it is much bigger than any of those stories. It is the illustration of a larger theme, a philosophy statement, a worldview that Dickens considers worthy of every person's attention and consideration. He expresses all of this as only Dickens can, by simply and eloquently stating he has penned a little "ghost of an idea" and he hopes it will "haunt" our houses pleasantly.

When introducing something new, it is good to begin with something old, something familiar. And so, Dickens, fully intending to tell a ghost story like no one has ever told before, kicks off the tale in a very traditional way by exclaiming "Marley was dead: to begin with." Right from the start we are drawn in. Everyone loves a good ghost story, and by announcing the name of the man who will return from the grave to thrill us with some sort of wild, weird, or wicked behavior, Dickens commands our full attention. Like an exclamation point coming at the beginning of the story rather than at the end, the ghost of Jacob Marley comes crashing in, causing us to sit up straight and view everything that follows with wide-eyed curiosity.

To date, I have never suffered the visitation of such a specter, but I have certainly experienced similar phenomenon that I am unable to chalk up to mere coincidence. When you spend as much time as I have with this particular tale, things happen, things that seem to be saying, "Sit up and pay attention!"

Once, a number of years ago on Thanksgiving Day, after we had consumed a fabulous feast followed by the traditional nap, my family and I decorated the Christmas tree in our living room. The following day, on Black Friday—the traditional day for so much merchandizing and profiteering that the sheer volume of sales would cause Jacob Marley to suffer an apoplectic, yet ecstatic, seizure—I ascended the stairs from the living room to my office above and pulled down from the shelf my well-worn rehearsal copy of *A Christmas Carol*. It was a bright, sunny day without a storm cloud in the sky, and very warm, which is typical weather that time of year for my aptly named hometown of Summerville, South Carolina. All of the windows in the house were shut and the air-conditioner was running. Just as I plunked the heavy volume down upon the reading desk and flopped back the bright red cover, a great gust of wind from who knows where came tearing around the house. It whirled and whistled beneath the eaves of the roof just outside my office window. I felt my clothing ripple, and the pages of the newly opened book fluttered as the wind came sweeping through the room. The window was closed, I tell you! Then, from downstairs I heard a crash and my wife's astonished voice almost in the same instant: "Did you feel that?"

We met in the living room to discover the Christmas tree had fallen. I started working on getting it upright again as my wife fetched the broom to sweep up the inevitably broken ornaments and decorations we were certain to discover. However, to our surprise—perhaps I should say amazement—nothing was broken except for one big, black ball with "Bah, Humbug!" written in white lettering across its surface. Needless to say, Charles Dickens, who claims in the story that lay open on my desk to be "standing in the spirit" at my elbow, had my full attention!

On two other occasions, someone (or some thing) seemed to be reaching into my world to grab my attention, and the attention of my audience I might add. Both of these incidences had to do with bells, which are discussed in more detail later. On the first occasion, I was performing at my beloved historic Timrod Library. I have told all kinds of stories there, but we always do *A Christmas Carol* at Christmastime. The atmosphere is just right for Dickens. The building is over a century old with creaking wooden floors, attic treasure furnishings, vintage paintings, and plenty of books. The walls of the room where I perform are lined with antique volumes. We employ two or three dozen candles to light the room, which of course is beautifully decorated for the holiday. It was in this perfect atmosphere when I uttered the words, "The night was waning fast. The church clock tower was even now striking three quarters past eleven," that the church clock tower across the street struck out the three-quarter Westminster chime. It was so perfectly timed, you'd have thought we rehearsed it. The effect was very exciting for both me and my audience. God bless those Methodists! Or did Methodism have anything to do with it?

I ask the question because the same thing happened on a second occasion at a different location. I was telling the story in the lobby of a local bank during my town's annual Dickens Ghost Walk, a progressive performance in which we tell different sections of the story at various local businesses in historic Summerville. Of course, the bank lobby serves as the setting for Scrooge's counting house. After hours, empty of customers and tellers, and with only the security lighting glowing in the corners of the room, the bank is a very quiet, even awe-inspiring place. In such an atmosphere, I can speak just above a whisper and be confident the audience can still hear every word.

We were coming to the end of the first stave of the story, and Jacob Marley was making his famous prediction in quiet, slow, and measured speech. "You will be haunted by three spirits....Expect the first tomorrow night when the bell tolls one....The next upon the second night at the same hour...and the third upon the last night when the final stroke of twelve has ceased to vibrate." Right on cue, the grandfather clock standing against the shadowed wall behind the gathered listeners struck out with such force that everyone jumped, turned toward the clock, and giggling nervously, looked back at me as if to say "How did you do that?" I assure you, it wasn't me. There is no way I could plan such a perfectly timed moment outside a well-equipped theater with an excellent technical director and a precisely played sound effect. However, I would never want to be found guilty of failing to seize such a golden moment, so I just winked at the audience and said, "Things that make you go 'hmmm'...." Without another word of explanation I turned and walked out of the bank to continue the tour.

I tell many, many stories. In fact, I recently added up the minutes it takes to tell each story in my repertoire and found that I can talk for over twenty-four hours without ever having to repeat myself. Of all of the stories, this is the one I have told the most. To date, I have performed *A Christmas Carol* over 150 times. I have toured the story from South Carolina to Alaska! Dickens performed the story on stages in America and Great Britain only 127 times, then promptly died. Consequently, I feel as if I am running on borrowed time. Perhaps that is the reason I say this story "haunts" me. It is such a part of my life that I usually take a long walk during the hot summer months and quote the entire story aloud to myself. I don't really know why I do this except that I love the characters and cannot resist the urge to return to the foggy streets of

London and check on Bob Cratchit and his family, Scrooge's nephew Fred, old Fezziwig, and all of the others. Ironically, just about the time American Independence Day rolls around on the calendar, I get the hankering to return to merry old England and visit with my British friends.

My colleague, storyteller Elizabeth Ellis, knows how to wrap her tongue around a good ghost story. In her book, *Prepare To Scare*, she says ghost stories at their core are expressions of metaphorical boogeymen who haunt our society. She explains ghost stories set in the past are tales of our regrets, our misdeeds, the mistakes from earlier times where we cannot return and make amends. She further explains monster stories contrast with ghost stories in that they are set in the future and serve as metaphorical tales of our fears, the collective consciousness of what might happen, the worries and dread of society. I think this is very true. It is especially true in *A Christmas Carol*.

I have my own ghost of Christmas Past that haunts my dreams every year. The specter arrives just before the first show of my annual Dickens performance tour. It is the Ghost of Regret. I find myself unable to sleep because I am sorry about all of the things I didn't do over the past several weeks when I was rehearsing. The "if onlys" crowd into my mind. If only I had rehearsed that tricky part in the third stave a little more. If only I had read the background article that's been laying on my desk for the past six weeks. If only I had skipped that movie with friends for one more dress rehearsal. If only this, if only that…but it's too late. I cannot change the past. What's done is done. Or in this case, what I have left undone must remain undone. This worrying and fretting is such an annual event that I suppose it is part of my rehearsal process.

One particular year the feeling was especially acute, and I found myself worrying even as I drove to the theater for the opening performance of the season. I prayed a quick prayer of desperation and as soon as I uttered the "amen," I looked up to see a liquor store perched on a hill above the highway. The name of the store was painted in large ghostly white lettering on the black awning over the door: "Scrooge's Spirits." My worry was immediately replaced with laughter. I drove to the theater smiling, reminded not to worry about the past I could not change, but just to enjoy the present. The show came off without a hitch.

Speaking of the present, that particular ghost has been my constant companion. He shows up every year without fail. With the sprinklings of his torch, the Ghost of Christmas Present smooths my way, makes everyone jolly and merry, and causes everything to be more exciting and festive. Once

ant presence in the Hartsfield-Jackson Atlanta
International Airport. I was traveling with two car-
ry-on items. One was a bright orange roll-aboard
suitcase that held a few CD recordings, some business cards, my personal copy of *A Christmas Carol,*
and my costume consisting of wool trousers, a
balloon-sleeved shirt with stand-up collar, brocade
vest, and a silk neckerchief. The other item was a
ridiculously large, dark brown top hat—the crowning accessory for my Dickens costume. The hat
would not fit into the bright orange suitcase without being crushed, so I was wearing it. As I strolled
through the busiest airport in the world, people
smiled, waved, wished me "Merry Christmas" and
one man even exclaimed "There goes Charles
Dickens!" I was inclined to believe all this goodwill
was merely the result of my festive top hat.

Then I came to the sixty-foot escalator that
would carry me, my top hat, the bright orange suitcase, and the unseen Ghost of Christmas Present
down to the train station in the basement level of
the airport. As I stepped onto the moving stairway
I thought to myself, "Some busy traveler in a rush
to catch their next flight will want to hurry down
this escalator. I'll move my suitcase to rest in front
of myself, so as to keep the left side clear for people
wishing to walk down the stairs." This is a common

courtesy when moving through the Atlanta airport. In fact, you'll often hear people in a hurry call out from the top of the escalator, "I have a tight connection. Passing on the left!" as they hurry down the stairs. Just as I started to move my suitcase, I lost my grip on the handle. Before I had time to react the suitcase started to slide down the escalator. Being made of hard, slick plastic, the thing picked up speed at an alarming rate and shot down that incline like a Russian bobsled chasing a bottle of vodka! My only recourse was to yell, "Passing on the left!"

Right on cue, everyone stepped to their right and turned to see my suitcase hurtling past. Miraculously, it did not fly off course, but went zooming by at least twenty people with alarming velocity. It hit the marble tile at the bottom, slid across the floor like a giant hockey puck, and disappeared from sight. I knew it had finally stopped when I heard a loud slam against an unseen wall of the train station lobby.

My first panicked thought was, "I've killed somebody!" I could see myself sitting in a funeral parlor explaining over and over again to mourners filing past the coffin how my suitcase had killed this poor, unsuspecting stranger. Running down the escalator, I assumed the posture of a repentant mourner by removing my top hat and holding it in my hand. As I rushed past my fellow travelers, I made hurried inquiries about the welfare of each person my suitcase had passed. No one reported an injury. The whole affair was so sudden, I think they were in complete shock and not exactly sure what had just happened. When I got to the bottom, I looked across the lobby and saw a tall, handsome airline employee in a bright red sport coat staring down at my suitcase, which was resting against the far wall. I ran toward my suitcase and the man smiled, held out his hand, and exclaimed, "Dude! That was the coolest thing I've ever seen!" We fist bumped, I picked up my luggage, which was not damaged, and stepped onto the train. The train doors closed and that was that. (Except for the gold sprinklings of the Spirit's torch I distinctly saw swirling through the air, ensuring everyone involved in this little holiday escapade lived happily ever after!)

They say these types of things come in threes, which makes me careful not to leave out the Ghost of Christmas Future. It is interesting to note that when Dickens introduces this most spectral of specters, he uses the darker and more sinister term "phantom" rather than "ghost" when referring to the Spirit that personifies our worst and most monstrous fears. A careful reading of the text shows Ebenezer Scrooge suffers from many fears of what the future might bring. Chief among them is the fear of being completely forgotten. He wrestles with this distinct possibility in a dismal and deserted churchyard overrun by grass and weeds. It is here that he comes to fully realize no amount of money, or talent, or business, or achievement will ensure the remembrance of a man's life. Rather, it is in the relationships he fosters, the time he invests, and the love he gives away that a man secures immortality in the minds of his friends.

Several years ago, I created a Ghost of Christmas Future for myself, a reminder of what is most important. For our annual Dickens Ghost Walk, I talked a local monument company into donating a 450-pound tombstone to be permanently placed in the front garden of Timrod Library. It is where we always begin our annual Dickens Ghost Walk with those famous words "Marley was dead: to begin with." Carved upon the stone is Jacob Marley's name with his birth and death dates beneath. Of course, Jacob Marley is a fictitious character and consequently the dates are arbitrary—except for the fact that I chose my own birthday of February 4 as the birthdate. I never look upon that cold, hard tablet witihout thinking about the course of my own life and how its entire history will be summarized with two dates etched upon a forgotten piece of stone, and whatever remains in the memories of my friends.

Ironically, Charles Dickens' holiday ghost story with its very sobering reminder of death is filled with the stuff of life: food, music, clothing, laughter, bells, children, weather, etc. These are the things I think about as I travel miles across the country every year on my annual Christmas tour. But I also think about them every other season of the year: when I am planting spring flowers, when I am sitting on the river bank waiting for the fish to bite on a summer's afternoon, when I am raking autumn leaves in the backyard. I don't think I will ever get away from this ghost story. Out of the blue a quotation from *A Christmas Carol* pops into my head and I am suddenly reminded of my resolution to live—to *really* live—in the Past, the Present, and the Future.

In this book I have recorded many of my thoughts and bound them to the pages of Mr. Dickens' *A Christmas Carol*. May they be a compliment to his work and not a distraction from it, for I would never wish to detract from Mr. Dickens' little "ghost of an idea." His story "haunts me pleasantly"

and I highly recommend it. Every single word. God
Bless Them, Every One!

A CHRISTMAS CAROL.

IN PROSE.

BEING

A Ghost Story of Christmas.

BY

CHARLES DICKENS

WITH ILLUSTRATIONS BY JOHN LEECH.

The KING PENGUIN *Books*

LONDON *and* NEW YORK

MCMXLVI

PREFACE

I have endeavored in this Ghostly little book, to raise the Ghost of an Idea, which shall not put my readers out of humor with themselves, with each other, with the season, or with me.

May it haunt their houses pleasantly, and no one wish to lay it.

Their faithful Friend and Servant,
C. D.
December, 1843

Marley's Ghost

STAVE ONE

MARLEY'S GHOST

Marley was dead: to begin with. There is no doubt whatever about that. The register of his burial was signed by the clergyman, the clerk, the undertaker, and the chief mourner. Scrooge signed it: and Scrooge's name was good upon 'Change, for anything he chose to put his hand to. Old Marley was as dead as a door-nail.

Mind! I don't mean to say that I know, of my own knowledge, what there is particularly dead about a door-nail. I might have been inclined, myself, to regard a coffin-nail as the deadest piece of ironmongery in the trade. But the wisdom of our ancestors is in the simile; and my unhallowed hands shall not disturb it, or the Country's done for. You will therefore permit me to repeat, emphatically, that Marley was as dead as a door-nail.

Scrooge knew he was dead? Of course he did. How could it be otherwise? Scrooge and he were partners for I don't know how many years. Scrooge was his sole executor, his sole administrator, his sole assign, his sole residuary legatee, his sole friend, and sole mourner. And even Scrooge was not so dreadfully cut up by the sad event, but that he was an excellent man of business on the very day of the funeral, and solemnized it with an undoubted bargain.

The mention of Marley's funeral brings me back to the point I started from. There is no doubt that Marley was dead. This must be distinctly understood, or nothing wonderful can come of the story I am going to relate. If we were not perfectly convinced that Hamlet's Father died before the play began, there would be nothing more remarkable in his taking a stroll at night, in an easterly wind, upon his own ramparts, than there would be in any other middle-aged gentleman rashly turning out after dark in a breezy spot—say Saint Paul's Churchyard for instance—literally to astonish his son's weak mind.

Scrooge never painted out Old Marley's name. There it stood, years afterwards, above the warehouse door: Scrooge and Marley. The firm was known as Scrooge and Marley. Sometimes people new to the business called Scrooge Scrooge, and sometimes Marley, but he answered to both names. It was all the same to him.

Oh! But he was a tight-fisted hand at the grindstone, Scrooge! a squeezing, wrenching, grasping, scraping, clutching, covetous old sinner! Hard and sharp as flint, from which no steel had ever struck out generous fire; secret, and self-contained, and solitary as an oyster. The cold within him froze his old features, nipped his pointed nose, shriveled his cheek, stiffened his gait; made his eyes red, his thin lips blue; and spoke out shrewdly in his grating voice. A frosty rime was on his head, and on his eyebrows, and his wiry chin. He carried his own low temperature always about with him; he iced his office in the dog-days; and didn't thaw it one degree at Christmas.

External heat and cold had little influence on Scrooge. No warmth could warm, nor wintry weather chill him. No wind that blew was bitterer than he, no falling snow was more intent upon its purpose, no pelting rain less open to entreaty. Foul weather didn't know where to have him. The heaviest rain, and snow, and hail, and sleet, could boast of the advantage over him in only one respect. They often "came down" handsomely, and Scrooge never did.

Nobody ever stopped him in the street to say, with gladsome looks, "My dear Scrooge, how are you? when will you come to see me?" No beggars implored him to bestow a trifle, no children asked him what it was o'clock, no man or woman ever once in all his life inquired the way to such and such a place, of Scrooge. Even the blind men's dogs appeared to know him; and when they saw him coming on, would tug their owners into doorways and up courts; and then would wag their tails as though they said, "no eye at all is better than an evil eye, dark master!"

But what did Scrooge care! It was the very thing he liked. To edge his way along the crowded paths of life, warning all human sympathy to keep its distance, was what the knowing ones call "nuts" to Scrooge.

WEATHER

He carried his own low temperature always about with him; he iced his office in the dog days; and didn't thaw it one degree at Christmas.

With the exception of Jack London in his short story, "To Build a Fire," no other writer describes the bone chilling effect of bitter cold better than Charles Dickens. His stories are not merely placed in well-described settings, they are atmospherical. You don't just read about London in December, you feel the shivering creep of a foggy dampness and brace for the wind that comes screaming round the corner, catching your breath as the blast sweeps past, tugging at your scarf and coat. I don't know about you, but I must always read Dickens with a blanket. And with *A Christmas Carol*, I also require hot buttered rum.

There is something—how does the Christmas song put it?—"thrilling" about the cold. It invigorates the body and sharpens the senses. As Dickens says, "the people wheezing up and down, beating their hands upon their breasts, and stamping their feet upon the pavement stones..." makes a "...rough, but brisk and not unpleasant kind of music." I often think of these words when I am greeting audience members as they jostle through the doors and into the glowing warmth of a theater lobby or restaurant dining room on a winter's evening.

At one particular performance in Lehi, Utah, there was so much snow and ice we delayed the show for the better part of an hour because the main highway leading to the theater was slick as glass and jammed with cars slipped sideways, a jackknifed tanker truck, and emergency vehicles everywhere. The unseasonable cold with traffic troubles piled on top might have caused people's personal barometric pressures to plummet. However, I don't recall a single person out of 500 who appeared to be the least bit out of sorts. The way folks jovially greeted one another, happily brushing the snow from each other's shoulders as they hugged and laughed, indicated that no one considered this situation a nightmare. No, they were well aware nightmares were the particular terror of people like Ebenezer Scrooge.

It is interesting to think of all the ways we describe personal feelings with metaphorical weather. For instance, a fellow with a temper is "hotheaded" and a gloomy person is known by their "stormy countenance." Many of these expressions are wintery. We speak of giving a cold stare, receiving the cold shoulder, and playing with a cool hand. When it comes to expressing fear, forgive the weather man pun, but it's a matter of degrees. There is quite a difference between suffering cold feet, being frozen with fear, or being chilled to the bone. However, in almost every case, these meteorological maladies are only temporary. With time and personal effort, the storm clears and we enjoy a "sunny disposition" or a "breezy attitude."

Not so with Ebenezer Scrooge. His affliction seems to be permanent and unalterable. To quote another beloved English writer, "It is always winter and never Christmas" because he suffers from a cold heart. Scrooge is a violent weather pattern unto himself. As he moves through his daily routine, most people avoid him as if he were an arctic storm. Like a dark thunder cloud, he rumbles and grumbles to himself and strikes out with verbal stabs of lightning toward anyone who gets too close. Several people valiantly try to use the art of persuasion to draw Scrooge out of his black mood and into the light, but it is no use. This tempest cannot be turned with logical argument. It will require a mighty working of the Spirit to not merely warm his frozen heart, but to forever shatter his ability to go back into such gloom and misery ever again.

Great storms are caused by opposing forces coming into a violent clash with one another. That is certainly true for Ebenezer Scrooge. In the span of a single night, his emotions are all over the weather map. The Past mixes the extreme high of sweet memory with the terrible low of sorrowful regret. The Present pushes abundant joy right up against the cold, hard realities of ignorance and want. The Future engulfs a brief moment of serene resignation at the death of Tiny Tim with a maelstrom of fear and doubt swirling through Scrooge's mind as he contemplates his own mortality.

In the made-for-television version of *A Christmas Carol* starring George C. Scott, this emotional hurricane is depicted with howling gusts of wind, deafening thunder, and blindingly bright flashes of lightning. These cataclysmic forces beat down upon Scrooge with relentless fury, driving him to his knees. Of course, the storm is not literal, it is metaphorical. There is a tempest in Scrooge's heart.

I don't know if you have ever experienced a hurricane, but if you have, then you well know the effect of passing through such an intense atmosphere. It may be you are experiencing such emotions right now as you read this book. It is a common condition of the human spirit to struggle through what the fifteenth-century Cistercian monk, John of the Cross, called "the dark night of the soul," and what St. Ignatious of Loyola called "times of desolation." Forgive me for quoting these ancient preachers. I realize when you are in the midst of a storm the last thing you need to hear is a sermon. So, I will not preach, but I do reserve the right to pray.

My prayer is this: When you finally emerge, may you be like Ebenezer Scrooge waking from his dream, laughing and crying at the same time.

This blessed bewilderment is the genuine emotion of a storm survivor. The laughter comes from the incredulity of the situation. Did that really happen? The tears come from the conviction that it really did. Both elements must be present. Laughter without the tears is the emotional state of a person in denial. Tears in the absence of laughter is the emotional state of a victim. But tearful laughter, the odd mix of sunshine and precipitation, not unlike the rainbow, is a sure sign that as a survivor you will never again be troubled by past regrets, present difficulties, or future fears; instead, you can now ride joyfully above the storm.

Once upon a time—of all the good days in the year, on Christmas Eve—old Scrooge sat busy in his counting-house. It was cold, bleak, biting weather: foggy withal: and he could hear the people in the court outside go wheezing up and down, beating their hands upon their breasts, and stamping their feet upon the pavement-stones to warm them. The city clocks had only just gone three, but it was quite dark already: it had not been light all day: and candles were flaring in the windows of the neighboring offices, like ruddy smears upon the palpable brown air. The fog came pouring in at every chink and keyhole, and was so dense without, that although the court was of the narrowest, the houses opposite were mere phantoms. To see the dingy cloud come drooping down, obscuring everything, one might have thought that Nature lived hard by, and was brewing on a large scale.

The door of Scrooge's counting-house was open that he might keep his eye upon his clerk, who in a dismal little cell beyond, a sort of tank, was copying letters. Scrooge had a very small fire, but the clerk's fire was so very much smaller that it looked like one coal. But he couldn't replenish it, for Scrooge kept the coal-box in his own room; and so surely as the clerk came in with the shovel, the master predicted that it would be necessary for them to part. Wherefore the clerk put on his white comforter, and tried to warm himself at the candle; in which effort, not being a man of a strong imagination, he failed.

"A merry Christmas, uncle! God save you!" cried a cheerful voice. It was the voice of Scrooge's nephew, who came upon him so quickly that this was the first intimation he had of his approach.

"Bah!" said Scrooge, "Humbug!"

He had so heated himself with rapid walking in the fog and frost, this nephew of Scrooge's, that he was all in a glow; his face was ruddy and handsome; his eyes sparkled, and his breath smoked again.

"Christmas a humbug, uncle!" said Scrooge's nephew. "You don't mean that, I am sure."

"I do," said Scrooge. "Merry Christmas! what right have you to be merry? what reason have you to be merry? You're poor enough."

"Come, then," returned the nephew gaily. "What right have you to be dismal? what reason have you to be morose? You're rich enough."

Scrooge having no better answer ready on the spur of the moment, said, "Bah!" again; and followed it up with "Humbug."

"Don't be cross, uncle," said the nephew.

"What else can I be" returned the uncle, "when I live in such a world of fools as this? Merry Christmas! Out upon merry Christmas! What's Christmas time to you but a time for paying bills without money; a time for finding yourself a year older, and not an hour richer; a time for balancing your books and having every item in 'em through a round dozen of months presented dead against you? If I could work my will," said Scrooge, indignantly, "every idiot who goes about with 'Merry Christmas,' on his lips, should be boiled with his own pudding, and buried with a stake of holly through his heart. He should!"

"Uncle!" pleaded the nephew.

"Nephew!" returned the uncle, sternly, "keep Christmas in your own way, and let me keep it in mine."

"Keep it!" repeated Scrooge's nephew. "But you don't keep it."

"Let me leave it alone, then," said Scrooge. "Much good may it do you! Much good it has ever done you!"

"There are many things from which I might have derived good, by which I have not profited, I dare say," returned the nephew: "Christmas among the rest. But I am sure I have always thought of Christmas time, when it has come round—apart from the veneration due to its sacred name and origin, if anything belonging to it can be apart from that—as a good time: a kind, forgiving, charitable, pleasant time: the only time I know of, in the long calendar of the year, when men and women seem by one consent to open their shut-up hearts freely, and to think of people below them as if they really were fellow-passengers to the grave, and not another race of creatures bound on other journeys. And therefore, uncle, though it has never put a scrap of gold or silver in my pocket, I believe that it has done me good, and will do me good; and I say, God bless it!"

The clerk in the tank involuntarily applauded: becoming immediately sensible of the impropriety, he poked the fire, and extinguished the last frail spark for ever.

"Let me hear another sound from you" said Scrooge, "and you'll keep your Christmas by losing your situation. You're quite a powerful speaker, sir," he added, turning to his nephew. "I wonder you don't go into Parliament."

"Don't be angry, uncle. Come! Dine with us to-morrow."

Scrooge said that he would see him—yes, indeed he did. He went the whole length of the expression, and said that he would see him in that extremity first.

"But why?" cried Scrooge's nephew. "Why?"

"Why did you get married?" said Scrooge.

"Because I fell in love."

"Because you fell in love!" growled Scrooge, as if that were the only one thing in the world more ridiculous than a merry Christmas. "Good afternoon!"

"Nay, uncle, but you never came to see me before that happened. Why give it as a reason for not coming now?"

"Good afternoon," said Scrooge.

"I want nothing from you; I ask nothing of you; why cannot we be friends?"

"Good afternoon," said Scrooge.

"I am sorry, with all my heart, to find you so resolute. We have never had any quarrel, to which I have been a party. But I have made the trial in homage to Christmas, and I'll keep my Christmas humor to the last. So A Merry Christmas, uncle!"

"Good afternoon!" said Scrooge.

"And A Happy New Year!"

"Good afternoon!" said Scrooge.

His nephew left the room without an angry word, notwithstanding. He stopped at the outer door to bestow the greetings of the season on the clerk, who, cold as he was, was warmer than Scrooge; for he returned them cordially.

"There's another fellow," muttered Scrooge; who overheard him: "my clerk, with fifteen shillings a-week, and a wife and family, talking about a merry Christmas. I'll retire to Bedlam."

This lunatic, in letting Scrooge's nephew out, had let two other people in. They were portly gentlemen, pleasant to behold, and now stood, with their hats off, in Scrooge's office. They had books and papers in their hands, and bowed to him.

"Scrooge and Marley's, I believe," said one of the gentlemen, referring to his list. "Have I the pleasure of addressing Mr. Scrooge, or Mr. Marley?"

"Mr. Marley has been dead these seven years," Scrooge replied. "He died seven years ago, this very night."

"We have no doubt his liberality is well represented by his surviving partner," said the gentleman, presenting his credentials.

It certainly was; for they had been two kindred spirits. At the ominous word "liberality," Scrooge frowned, and shook his head, and handed the credentials back.

"At this festive season of the year, Mr. Scrooge," said the gentleman, taking up a pen, "it is more than usually desirable that we should make some slight provision for the Poor and destitute, who suffer greatly at the present time. Many thousands are in want of common necessaries; hundreds of thousands are in want of common comforts, sir."

"Are there no prisons?" asked Scrooge.

"Plenty of prisons," said the gentleman, laying down the pen again.

"And the Union workhouses?" demanded Scrooge. "Are they still in operation?"

"They are. Still," returned the gentleman, "I wish I could say they were not."

"The Treadmill and the Poor Law are in full vigour, then?" said Scrooge.

"Both very busy, sir."

"Oh! I was afraid, from what you said at first, that something had occurred to stop them in their useful course," said Scrooge. "I'm very glad to hear it."

"Under the impression that they scarcely furnish Christian cheer of mind or body to the multitude," returned the gentleman, "a few of us are endeavoring to raise a fund to buy the Poor some meat and drink, and means of warmth. We choose this time, because it is a time, of all others, when Want is keenly felt, and Abundance rejoices. What shall I put you down for?"

"Nothing!" Scrooge replied.

"You wish to be anonymous?"

"I wish to be left alone," said Scrooge. "Since you ask me what I wish, gentlemen, that is my answer. I don't make merry myself at Christmas, and I can't afford to make idle people merry. I help to support the establishments I have mentioned: they cost enough: and those who are badly off must go there."

"Many can't go there; and many would rather die."

"If they would rather die," said Scrooge, "they had better do it, and decrease the surplus population. Besides— excuse me—I don't know that."

"But you might know it," observed the gentleman.

"It's not my business," Scrooge returned. "It's enough for a man to understand his own business, and not to interfere with other people's. Mine occupies me constantly. Good afternoon, gentlemen!"

Seeing clearly that it would be useless to pursue their point, the gentlemen withdrew. Scrooge resumed his labors with an improved opinion of himself, and in a more facetious temper than was usual with him.

CHRIST

But I am sure I have always thought of Christmas time,
when it has come round—apart from the veneration
due to its sacred name and origin, if anything belong-
ing to it can be apart from that—as a good time: a
kind, forgiving, charitable, pleasant time.

In this collection of essays, I have tried my best not
to preach (much), but on this particular point I
am going to pound the pulpit just a bit. However,
I'm not pointing a finger at the sinner so much as
the saint. Over the years, I have met many a pious
person who complains Dickens' little ghost story
is not Christian enough. They fear its popular-
ity is partly to blame for the secularization of the
sacred holiday. I met one very earnest gentleman

who re-wrote the entire story, making Ebenezer Scrooge a "liberal judge that kicked prayer out of schools," and after a series of heavenly visitations he gets his heart right and declares "Jesus is the reason for the season!" (You hear that thumping sound? That's Charles Dickens rolling over in his grave.)

I shall refrain from pointing out to the well-meaning gentleman that the quotation at the top of this page, taken directly from the novel, is exactly the same religious sentiment, only written with a dignity and reverence his bumper sticker slogan sadly lacks. I will also charitably neglect to point out his hastily rewritten version of a classic nineteenth-century English novel is an act of literary piracy incongruous with the basic tenets of Christian decorum and ethics. I shall refrain. But please indulge me as I make a case for the "Christianity" of *A Christmas Carol*. To quote the Apostle Paul, "I speak as a fool."

To begin with, Charles Dickens is not a clergyman. He is a storyteller. And as such, it is not his purpose to preach, but to illustrate. I often explain it this way. A student is expected to read a text and know what it says. A teacher is expected to read a text and explain what it means. A preacher is expected to tell us what action we should take based upon the meaning of the text. But a storyteller's job is to simply paint a picture of what the student, the teacher, and the preacher are all talking about. That's what Dickens is doing, and he does it very well. He is not ignoring or secularizing the story of Jesus' birth. In fact, he makes direct references to it in several places. Instead, he is contextualizing the story. He is painting a picture of what Christmas should look like in the streets of London. He is endeavoring to answer the question, "What difference does it make?" Short answer: a lot! Or at least it should.

I made a reference to the Apostle Paul. Let's compare a text from his Letter to the Galatians, which discusses the Holy Spirit, to Charles Dickens' story about the Christmas Spirit. For good measure we could cross-reference hundreds of scriptures for this little sermonette, but in keeping with the holiday theme we will restrict ourselves to the accounts of Jesus' birth as recorded by Saints Matthew and Luke.

But the fruit of the Spirit is love, joy, peace, long-suffering, gentleness, goodness, faith, meekness, temperance: against such there is no law. (Galatians 5:22-23)

1. Joy - The face of every person Scrooge encounters in the street evidences a joyful heart: the boy singing through the keyhole, the young

lads sliding on the icy pavement, the bustling merchants and customers in the market, the party attendees, the churchgoers, etc. All of these people in the midst of their expectant preparations for something wonderful are not unlike the Wise Men of scripture. *When they saw the star, they rejoiced with exceeding great joy.* (Matthew 2:10)

2. Peace - In the busy streets, Scrooge witnesses an exchange between harried strangers. Their angry words are transformed into good humor by the Ghost of Christmas Present. It's as if— what's the saying?—Something has come over them. *Glory to God in the highest, and on earth peace, good will toward men.* (Luke 2:14)

3. Long-suffering - If there was ever a portrait of "one who suffers long," a person who is patiently waiting for things to be set right, it would be a picture of Bob Cratchit. In his ever faithful waiting and watching and hoping, he is not unlike the aged prophet Simeon who waited all his life to see the salvation of Israel. *And it was revealed unto him by the Holy Ghost, that he should not see death, before he had seen the Lord's Christ.* (Luke 2:26)

4. Gentleness - Belle, Scrooge's fiancee, breaks their engagement with such a soft speech and gentle manner that her own heartbreak even in the act of doing what must be done is never in question. This gentleness is a reflection of the biblical character of Joseph who similarly considered a release from his engagement to Mary but was unwilling to cause her public shame or humiliation. *Then Joseph her husband, being a just man and not willing to make her a public example, was minded to put her away privily.* (Matthew 1:19)

5. Goodness - We often use this word when describing a generous person. If that be the case, then the portly gentlemen visiting Scrooge's office to collect donations for the poor are good examples. *He hath filled the hungry with good things.* (Luke 1:53a)

6. Faith - When Fred expresses confidence his Uncle Scrooge will come around sooner or later and that he "shook him" with his Christmas greetings, we see a picture of faith, the substance of things hoped for, and the evidence of things not seen. This attitude of confident expectancy for seemingly impossible things parallels that of several biblical characters from the Christmas story, with Mary being the prime

example. *And blessed is she that believed: for there shall be a performance of those things which were told her from the Lord.* (Luke 1:43)

7. Meekness - According to the Merriam-Webster Dictionary, meekness is the ability to endure injury with patience and without resentment. Can there be a better example of this quality than what we see in Tiny Tim? Is he not a reflection of the low estate in which Christ himself spent his own childhood? *And the grace of God was upon Him.* (Luke 2:40)

8. Temperance - Most often defined as self-control, this character trait is seen in the Cratchit household during the Christmas feast. First, we see a comic example when the little ones "cram spoons into their mouths, lest they should shriek for goose before their turn came to be helped." A second and more serious example follows when Bob Cratchit reminds his wife that she should hold her tongue when expressing her thoughts about Ebenezer Scrooge. Both of these are pictures of placing one's self under a restraint for the benefit of others, which is the most noble reason to exercise self-control. The same character trait is exhibited by the Christ child when he lays aside all his rights and

privileges as the Son of God and places himself under his earthly parents' authority. *And he went down with them...and was subject unto them.* (Luke 2:51)

9. Love - Even though it is listed first, I saved this one for last. It is definitely the biggie. In fact, it is so big it requires a crescendo of oratory like you might hear at the conclusion of a rousing sermon. So here we go. Hold on to your prayer books.

In this passage we have considered the various "Fruits of the Spirit" and how they are reflected in the story Mr. Dickens has given to the world. In so doing, we have made a case for the fact that Mr. Dickens was not in any way guilty of secularizing the holiday of Christmas, but was indeed very mindful of its sacred origin. However, it is not sufficient to merely prove the religiosity of another man's work, for that is not the point of a sermon. The purpose of any pulpit speech is to encourage self-examination and introspection, a personal reckoning with ultimate truth. To that end, I ask any of you who may think Mr. Dickens did not know the *real* meaning of Christmas—do you?

In this story, Mr. Dickens has presented us with a picture of a man who is completely undeserving of even so much as the benefit of the doubt, let alone forgiveness, and yet every single soul who has ever been wronged, cheated, slandered, or abused by one Ebenezer Scrooge willingly, joyfully, and immediately forgives his every sin. And by so doing, these people have performed the greatest act of Christian charity anyone can bestow upon a fellow human being. In forgiveness of their fellow man, they have given testimony to the fact that we are all lost in the darkness of our trespasses and in great need of forgiveness ourselves. In other words, they have given, in homage to His name's sake and in recognition of His holy nativity, the very love of Christ. That is the essence of the Christian faith: to love, even as Christ has loved you. Now, go forth, and do likewise!

Thus endeth the sermon for today. Let us pray. "God Bless Us, Every One!" Amen.

Meanwhile the fog and darkness thickened so, that people ran about with flaring links, proffering their services to go before horses in carriages, and conduct them on their way. The ancient tower of a church, whose gruff old bell was always peeping slyly down at Scrooge out of a gothic window in the wall, became invisible, and struck the hours and quarters in the clouds, with tremulous vibrations afterwards, as if its teeth were chattering in its frozen head up there. The cold became intense. In the main street, at the corner of the court, some laborers were repairing the gas-pipes, and had lighted a great fire in a brazier, round which a party of ragged men and boys were gathered: warming their hands and winking their eyes before the blaze in rapture. The water-plug being left in solitude, its overflowings sullenly congealed, and turned to misanthropic ice. The brightness of the shops where holly sprigs and berries crackled in the lamp-heat of the windows, made pale faces ruddy as they passed. Poulterers' and grocers' trades became a splendid joke: a glorious pageant, with which it was next to impossible to believe that such dull principles as bargain and sale had anything to do. The Lord Mayor, in the stronghold of the mighty Mansion House, gave orders to his fifty cooks and butlers to keep Christmas as a Lord Mayor's household should; and even the little tailor, whom he had fined five shillings on the previous Monday for being drunk and blood-thirsty in the streets, stirred up to-morrow's pudding in his garret, while his lean wife and the baby sallied out to buy the beef.

Foggier yet, and colder! Piercing, searching, biting cold. If the good Saint Dunstan had but nipped the Evil Spirit's nose with a touch of such weather as that, instead of using his familiar weapons, then indeed he would have roared to lusty purpose. The owner of one scant young nose, gnawed and mumbled by the hungry cold as bones are gnawed by dogs, stooped down at Scrooge's keyhole to regale him with a Christmas carol: but at the first sound of

"God bless you merry gentleman!
May nothing you dismay!"

Scrooge seized the ruler with such energy of action, that the singer fled in terror, leaving the keyhole to the fog and even more congenial frost.

At length the hour of shutting up the counting-house arrived. With an ill-will Scrooge dismounted from his stool, and tacitly admitted the fact to the expectant clerk in the Tank, who instantly snuffed his candle out, and put on his hat.

"You'll want all day to-morrow, I suppose?' said Scrooge.

"If quite convenient, Sir."

"It's not convenient," said Scrooge, "and it's not fair. If I was to stop half-a-crown for it, you'd think yourself ill used, I'll be bound?"

The clerk smiled faintly.

"And yet," said Scrooge, "you don't think me ill-used, when I pay a day's wages for no work."

The clerk observed that it was only once a year.

"A poor excuse for picking a man's pocket every twenty-fifth of December!" said Scrooge, buttoning his great-coat to the chin. "But I suppose you must have the whole day. Be here all the earlier next morning!"

The clerk promised that he would; and Scrooge walked out with a growl. The office was closed in a twinkling, and the clerk, with the long ends of his white comforter dangling below his waist (for he boasted no great-coat), went down a slide on Cornhill, at the end of a lane of boys, twenty times, in honor of its being Christmas-eve, and then ran home to Camden Town as hard as he could pelt, to play at blindman's-buff.

Scrooge took his melancholy dinner in his usual melancholy tavern; and having read all the newspapers, and beguiled the rest of the evening with his banker's-book, went home to bed. He lived in chambers which had once belonged to his deceased partner. They were a gloomy suite of rooms, in a lowering pile of building up a yard, where it had so little business to be, that one could scarcely help fancying it must have run there when it was a young house, playing at hide-and-seek with other houses, and had forgotten the way out again. It was old enough now, and dreary enough, for nobody lived in it but Scrooge, the other rooms being all let out as offices. The yard was so dark that even Scrooge, who knew its every stone, was fain to grope with his hands. The fog and frost so hung about the black old gateway of the house, that it seemed as if the Genius of the Weather sat in mournful meditation on the threshold.

Now, it is a fact, that there was nothing at all particular about the knocker on the door, except that it was very large. It is also a fact, that Scrooge had seen it night and morning during his whole residence in that place; also that Scrooge had as little of what is called fancy about him as any man in the City of London, even including—which is a bold word—the corporation, aldermen, and livery. Let it also be borne in mind that Scrooge had not bestowed one thought on Marley, since his last mention of his seven-years' dead partner that afternoon. And then let any man explain to me, if he can, how it happened that Scrooge, having his key in the lock of the door, saw in the knock-er, without its undergoing any intermediate process of change: not a knocker, but Marley's face.

Marley's face. It was not in impenetrable shadow as the other objects in the yard were, but had a dismal light about it, like a bad lobster in a dark cellar. It was not angry or fe-rocious, but looked at Scrooge as Marley used to look: with ghostly spectacles turned up upon its ghostly forehead. The hair was curiously stirred, as if by breath or hot-air; and though the eyes were wide open, they were perfectly motionless. That, and its livid color, made it horrible; but its horror seemed to be, in spite of the face and beyond its control, rather than a part of its own expression.

As Scrooge looked fixedly at this phenomenon, it was a knocker again.

To say that he was not startled, or that his blood was not conscious of a terrible sensation to which it had been a stranger from infancy, would be untrue. But he put his hand upon the key he had relinquished, turned it sturdily, walked in, and lighted his candle.

He did pause, with a moment's irresolution, before he shut the door; and he did look cautiously behind it first, as if he half-expected to be terrified with the sight of Marley's pigtail sticking out into the hall. But there was nothing on the back of the door, except the screws and nuts that held the knocker on; so he said "Pooh, pooh!" and closed it with a bang.

The sound resounded through the house like thunder. Every room above, and every cask in the wine-merchant's cellars below, appeared to have a separate peal of echoes of its own. Scrooge was not a man to be frightened by echoes. He fastened the door, and walked across the hall, and up the stairs: slowly too: trimming his candle as he went.

You may talk vaguely about driving a coach-and-six up a good old flight of stairs, or through a bad young Act of Parliament; but I mean to say you might have got a hearse up that staircase, and taken it broad-wise, with the splinter-bar towards the wall, and the door towards the balustrades: and done it easy. There was plenty of width for that, and room to spare; which is perhaps the reason why Scrooge thought he saw a locomotive hearse going on before him in the gloom. Half a dozen gas-lamps out of the street wouldn't have lighted the entry too well, so you may suppose that it was pretty dark with Scrooge's dip.

Up Scrooge went, not caring a button for that: darkness is cheap, and Scrooge liked it. But before he shut his heavy door, he walked through his rooms to see that all was right. He had just enough recollection of the face to desire to do that.

Sitting room, bed-room, lumber-room. All as they should be. Nobody under the table, nobody under the sofa; a small fire in the grate; spoon and basin ready; and the little saucepan of gruel (Scrooge had a cold in his head) upon the hob. Nobody under the bed; nobody in the closet; nobody in his dressing-gown, which was hanging up in a suspicious attitude against the wall. Lumber-room as usual. Old fire-guard, old shoes, two fish-baskets, washing-stand on three legs, and a poker.

Quite satisfied, he closed his door, and locked himself in; double-locked himself in, which was not his custom. Thus secured against surprise, he took off his cravat; put on his dressing-gown and slippers, and his night-cap; and sat down before the fire to take his gruel.

It was a very low fire indeed; nothing on such a bitter night. He was obliged to sit close to it, and brood over it, before he could extract the least sensation of warmth from such a handful of fuel. The fire-place was an old one, built by some Dutch merchant long ago, and paved all round with quaint Dutch tiles, designed to illustrate the Scriptures. There were Cains and Abels; Pharaoh's daughters, Queens of Sheba, Angelic messengers descending through the air on clouds like feather-beds, Abrahams, Belshazzars, Apostles putting off to sea in butter-boats, hundreds of figures, to attract his thoughts; and yet that face of Marley, seven years dead, came like the ancient

Prophet's rod, and swallowed up the whole. If each smooth tile had been a blank at first, with power to shape some picture on its surface from the disjointed fragments of his thoughts, there would have been a copy of old Marley's head on every one.

"Humbug!" said Scrooge; and walked across the room.

After several turns, he sat down again. As he threw his head back in the chair, his glance happened to rest upon a bell, a disused bell, that hung in the room, and communicated for some purpose now forgotten with a chamber in the highest story of the building. It was with great astonishment, and with a strange, inexplicable dread, that as he looked, he saw this bell begin to swing. It swung so softly in the outset that it scarcely made a sound; but soon it rang out loudly, and so did every bell in the house.

This might have lasted half a minute, or a minute, but it seemed an hour. The bells ceased as they had begun, together. They were succeeded by a clanking noise, deep down below; as if some person were dragging a heavy chain over the casks in the wine-merchant's cellar. Scrooge then remembered to have heard that ghosts in haunted houses were described as dragging chains.

BELLS

His glance happened to rest upon a bell, a disused bell...but soon it rang out loudly, and so did every bell in the house.

Dickens introduces the theme of bells by describing a "gruff old bell" that was always peeping slyly down from the gothic window of an ancient church tower into the dark, cramped, cold countinghouse of Ebenezer Scrooge. Shortly after this description, Dickens begins to develop the theme with a reference to St. Dunstan, the patron saint of bell ringers. As the story goes, St. Dunstan was a metalworker who pioneered the art of crafting bells for the the great church towers of England. On one occasion the Devil came to Dunstan's humble and grubby little cell disguised as an old man, but the wary saint recognized the evil shapeshifter, seized his hot iron tongs from the fire, and clamped them onto the Devil's nose. The Devil struggled and screamed but Dunstan held on until he triumphed over the Father of Lies and sent him howling down the street. When people heard the noise, they came to Dunstan's cell inquiring about the ruckus and he said to them, "These are the tricks of the Devil, who tries to trap us with his snares whenever he can. But if we remain firm in the service of Christ, we can easily defeat him with His help, and he will flee from us in confusion." St. Dunstan was a beloved figure of English church history and folklore and this one quick reference to his "familiar weapons" would have reminded Dickens' readers of the old legend.

The reference to St. Dunstan, a venerated saint from the Middle Ages, is embedded in a lengthy description of the weather that includes dense, billowing banks of fog and frozen mist. These details will eventually be combined with a "glimpse of the invisible world" where the Ghost of Jacob Marley makes it quite clear Scrooge is surrounded by, to use a Biblical phrase, "a great cloud of witnesses" who are watching as he is put to the test in the battle between good and evil. Lest we miss this point or we lose sight of it in the merrier and brighter scenes of the story, Dickens references the Devil again near the very end of the novel when a character speaks of Scrooge's death in exclaiming, "Well, Old Scratch has got his own at last, hey?" In other words, the failure of Ebenezer Scrooge to resist the Devil will result in the damnation of his mortal soul.

And you thought this was just a fun little ghost story for Christmas. Oh, not so. Not so, at all. Dickens is very Church of England in this respect. This story isn't "just for fun." It is a morality play, not unlike those of the Middle Ages performed on the steps of ancient cathedrals. Admittedly, it is a melodrama and does not fail to delight and entertain, even evoking laughter from the reader, but nonetheless it is a story with cosmic consequences, and consequently we are called to serious contemplation by the bells of the church.

Beginning with the tolling of a cold and somber tone from the bell in the church tower, the entire story is punctuated with the ringing of bells. All the bells in Scrooge's house spontaneously clash and clang just before Marley's entrance to his apartment. This cacophony of brass, bronze, copper, and tin is an auditory representation of Scrooge's disturbed mind. Regretful memories of the past, troublesome situations in the present, and his constant fear of the future are all clamoring for his attention. It is his aim to sleep, but in this agitated mental state, as the saying goes, there is no rest for the weary. Marley breaks in upon Scrooge's worried mind in a most dramatic and very real fashion, predicting that at the tolling of the hours Scrooge will be haunted by three spirits. And indeed, the arrival of each ghost is announced by the ringing of bells. These chimes, not unlike the carillons of great cathedrals, serve as a steadying force. For the faithful they are a call to pray the hours. For Scrooge, they serve as a way of organizing his thoughts and taking one thing at a time, which is the only way to deal with a disturbed and troubled mind.

Upon the stroke of one come the regrets of his past. The chiming of the quarter hour, the half, the third quarter, and then the hour itself worries and frightens Scrooge as he awaits the coming of the first spirit. But when it finally arrives, the Ghost of Christmas Past reveals itself not as a terrifying phantom, but a rather curious and non-threatening form of light, providing clarity to Scrooge as he views scenes that have long haunted his memory.

When the bell tolls again, the same as before, upon the stroke of one, Scrooge is more prepared and perhaps a bit less apprehensive. Having wrestled with the ghosts of his past and put them to bed, so to speak, he grows to enjoy the company of the Ghost of Christmas Present and begins to learn how to view his current situation not as a life filled with troubles and cares, but as an adventure with all the promise of a joyful and happing ending.

However, the bright and merry scenes enjoyed with the Ghost of Christmas Present, are rudely and horrifically interrupted by the tolling of a different bell, not the chime of the first hour of the new day, but the stroke of midnight, the dark hour of death. It is in this hour that Scrooge must reckon with the Ghost of Christmas Future and come face to face with his greatest fear, the inevitability of his own mortality. Thankfully, in his darkest moment, Scrooge passes the moral test. He throws himself upon the mercy of heaven. Accompanied by the joyous pealing of church bells signaling a wondrous change of heart, Ebenezer Scrooge, literally on his knees like a penitent sinner, thanks Jacob Marley for his intervention and vows to keep Christmas all the year.

Suddenly, the story is transformed from a morality play to a miracle play, and Scrooge becomes the patron saint of the poor. Then with the merry church bells as background music, we finally witness a "fun little ghost story for Christmas," as Scrooge becomes almost unrecognizable to the people who know him best; his old self is a vaguely remembered shadow, a ghost that does not frighten, but instead invokes laughter.

And what is to be said of that? Well, to quote Mr. Dickens: "Clash, clang, hammer, ding, dong bell. Bell, dong, ding, hammer, clang, clash. Oh, glorious, glorious!"

The cellar-door flew open with a booming sound, and then he heard the noise much louder, on the floors below; then coming up the stairs; then coming straight towards his door.

"It's humbug still!" said Scrooge. "I won't believe it."

His color changed though, when, without a pause, it came on through the heavy door, and passed into the room before his eyes. Upon its coming in, the dying flame leaped up, as though it cried "I know him! Marley's Ghost!" and fell again.

The same face: the very same. Marley in his pig-tail, usual waistcoat, tights, and boots; the tassels on the latter bristling, like his pigtail, and his coat-skirts, and the hair upon his head. The chain he drew was clasped about his middle. It was long, and wound about him like a tail; and it was made (for Scrooge observed it closely) of cash-boxes, keys, padlocks, ledgers, deeds, and heavy purses wrought in steel. His body was transparent: so that Scrooge, observing him, and looking through his waistcoat, could see the two buttons on his coat behind.

Scrooge had often heard it said that Marley had no bowels, but he had never believed it until now.

No, nor did he believe it even now. Though he looked the phantom through and through, and saw it standing before him; though he felt the chilling influence of its death-cold eyes; and marked the very texture of the folded kerchief bound about its head and chin, which wrapper he had not observed before: he was still incredulous, and fought against his senses.

"How now!" said Scrooge, caustic and cold as ever. "What do you want with me?"

"Much!"—Marley's voice, no doubt about it.

"Who are you?"

"Ask me who I was."

"Who were you then?" said Scrooge, raising his voice. "You're particular—for a shade." He was going to say "to a shade," but substituted this, as more appropriate.

"In life I was your partner, Jacob Marley."

"Can you—can you sit down?" asked Scrooge, looking doubtfully at him.

"I can."

"Do it then."

Scrooge asked the question, because he didn't know whether a ghost so transparent might find himself in a condition to take a chair; and felt that in the event of its being impossible, it might involve the necessity of an embarrassing explanation. But the ghost sat down on the opposite side of the fire-place, as if he were quite used to it.

"You don't believe in me," observed the Ghost.

"I don't," said Scrooge.

"What evidence would you have of my reality, beyond that of your senses?"

"I don't know," said Scrooge.

"Why do you doubt your senses?"

"Because," said Scrooge, "a little thing affects them. A slight disorder of the stomach makes them cheats. You may be an undigested bit of beef, a blot of mustard, a crumb of cheese, a fragment of an underdone potato. There's more of gravy than of grave about you, whatever you are!"

Scrooge was not much in the habit of cracking jokes, nor did he feel, in his heart, by any means waggish then. The truth is, that he tried to be smart, as a means of distracting his own attention, and keeping down his terror; for the specter's voice disturbed the very marrow in his bones.

To sit, staring at those fixed, glazed eyes, in silence for a moment, would play, Scrooge felt, the very deuce with him. There was something very awful, too, in the specter's being provided with an infernal atmosphere of its own. Scrooge could not feel it himself, but this was clearly the case; for though the Ghost sat perfectly motionless, its hair, and skirts, and tassels, were still agitated as by the hot vapor from an oven.

"You see this toothpick?" said Scrooge, returning quickly to the charge, for the reason just assigned; and wishing, though it were only for a second, to divert the vision's stony gaze from himself.

"I do," replied the Ghost.

"You are not looking at it," said Scrooge.

"But I see it," said the Ghost, "notwithstanding."

"Well!" returned Scrooge. "I have but to swallow this, and be for the rest of my days persecuted by a legion of goblins, all of my own creation. Humbug, I tell you—humbug!"

At this, the spirit raised a frightful cry, and shook its chain with such a dismal and appalling noise, that Scrooge held on tight to his chair, to save himself from falling in a swoon. But how much greater was his horror, when the phantom taking off the bandage round its head, as if it were too warm to wear in-doors, its lower jaw dropped down upon its breast!

Scrooge fell upon his knees, and clasped his hands before his face.

"Mercy!" he said. "Dreadful apparition, why do you trouble me?"

"Man of the worldly mind!" replied the Ghost, "do you believe in me or not?"

"I do," said Scrooge. "I must. But why do spirits walk the earth, and why do they come to me?"

"It is required of every man," the Ghost returned, "that the spirit within him should walk abroad among his fellow-men, and travel far and wide; and if that spirit goes not forth in life, it is condemned to do so after death. It is doomed to wander through the world—oh, woe is me!—and witness what it cannot share, but might have shared on earth, and turned to happiness!"

Again the specter raised a cry, and shook its chain, and wrung its shadowy hands.

"You are fettered," said Scrooge, trembling. "Tell me why?"

"I wear the chain I forged in life," replied the Ghost. "I made it link by link, and yard by yard; I girded it on of my own free will, and of my own free will I wore it. Is its pattern strange to you?"

Scrooge trembled more and more.

"Or would you know," pursued the Ghost, "the weight and length of the strong coil you bear yourself? It was full as heavy and as long as this, seven Christmas Eves ago. You have labored on it, since. It is a ponderous chain!"

Scrooge glanced about him on the floor, in the expectation of finding himself surrounded by some fifty or sixty fathoms of iron cable: but he could see nothing.

"Jacob," he said, imploringly. "Old Jacob Marley, tell me more. Speak comfort to me, Jacob."

"I have none to give," the Ghost replied. "It comes from other regions, Ebenezer Scrooge, and is conveyed by other ministers, to other kinds of men. Nor can I tell you what I would. A very little more, is all permitted to me. I cannot rest, I cannot stay, I cannot linger anywhere. My spirit never walked beyond our counting-house—mark me!—in life my spirit never roved beyond the narrow limits of our money-changing hole; and weary journeys lie before me!"

It was a habit with Scrooge, whenever he became thoughtful, to put his hands in his breeches pockets. Pondering on what the Ghost had said, he did so now, but without lifting up his eyes, or getting off his knees.

"You must have been very slow about it, Jacob," Scrooge observed, in a business-like manner, though with humility and deference.

"Slow!" the Ghost repeated.

"Seven years dead," mused Scrooge. "And travelling all the time?"

"The whole time," said the Ghost. "No rest, no peace. Incessant torture of remorse."

"You travel fast?" said Scrooge.

"On the wings of the wind," replied the Ghost.

"You might have got over a great quantity of ground in seven years," said Scrooge.

The Ghost, on hearing this, set up another cry, and clanked its chain so hideously in the dead silence of the night, that the Ward would have been justified in indicting it for a nuisance.

"Oh! captive, bound, and double-ironed," cried the phantom, "not to know, that ages of incessant labour by immortal creatures, for this earth must pass into eternity before the good of which it is susceptible is all developed. Not to know that any Christian spirit working kindly in its little sphere, whatever it may be, will find its mortal life too short for its vast means of usefulness. Not to know that no space of regret can make amends for one life's opportunities misused! Yet such was I! Oh! such was I!"

"But you were always a good man of business, Jacob," faultered Scrooge, who now began to apply this to himself.

"Business!" cried the Ghost, wringing its hands again. "Mankind was my business. The common welfare was my business; charity, mercy, forbearance, and benevolence, were, all, my business. The dealings of my trade were but a drop of water in the comprehensive ocean of my business!"

It held up its chain at arm's length, as if that were the cause of all its unavailing grief, and flung it heavily upon the ground again.

"At this time of the rolling year," the specter said, "I suffer most. Why did I walk through crowds of fellow-beings with my eyes turned down, and never raise them to that blessed Star which led the Wise Men to a poor abode? Were there no poor homes to which its light would have conducted me!"

Scrooge was very much dismayed to hear the spectre going on at this rate, and began to quake exceedingly.

"Hear me!" cried the Ghost. "My time is nearly gone."

"I will," said Scrooge. "But don't be hard upon me! Don't be flowery, Jacob! Pray!"

"How it is that I appear before you in a shape that you can see, I may not tell. I have sat invisible beside you many and many a day."

It was not an agreeable idea. Scrooge shivered, and wiped the perspiration from his brow.

"That is no light part of my penance," pursued the Ghost. "I am here to-night to warn you, that you have yet a chance and hope of escaping my fate. A chance and hope of my procuring, Ebenezer."

"You were always a good friend to me," said Scrooge. "Thank'ee!"

"You will be haunted," resumed the Ghost, "by Three Spirits."

Scrooge's countenance fell almost as low as the Ghost's had done.

"Is that the chance and hope you mentioned, Jacob?" he demanded, in a faltering voice.

"It is."

"I—I think I'd rather not," said Scrooge.

"Without their visits," said the Ghost, "you cannot hope to shun the path I tread. Expect the first to-morrow, when the bell tolls one."

"Couldn't I take 'em all at once, and have it over, Jacob?" hinted Scrooge.

"Expect the second on the next night at the same hour. The third upon the next night when the last stroke of twelve has ceased to vibrate. Look to see me no more; and look that, for your own sake, you remember what has passed between us!"

When it had said these words, the specter took its wrapper from the table, and bound it round its head, as before. Scrooge knew this, by the smart sound its teeth made, when the jaws were brought together by the bandage. He ventured to raise his eyes again, and found his supernatural visitor confronting him in an erect attitude, with its chain wound over and about its arm.

The apparition walked backward from him; and at every step it took, the window raised itself a little, so that when the specter reached it, it was wide open. It beckoned Scrooge to approach, which he did. When they were within two paces of each other, Marley's Ghost held up its hand, warning him to come no nearer. Scrooge stopped.

Not so much in obedience, as in surprise and fear: for on the raising of the hand, he became sensible of confused noises in the air; incoherent sounds of lamentation and regret; wailings inexpressibly sorrowful and self-accusatory. The specter, after listening for a moment, joined in the mournful dirge; and floated out upon the bleak, dark night.

Scrooge followed to the window: desperate in his curiosity. He looked out.

The air was filled with phantoms, wandering hither and thither in restless haste, and moaning as they went. Every one of them wore chains like Marley's Ghost; some few (they might be guilty governments) were linked together; none were free. Many had been personally known to Scrooge in their lives. He had been quite familiar with one old ghost, in a white waistcoat, with a monstrous iron safe attached to its ankle, who cried piteously at being unable to assist a wretched woman with an infant, whom it saw below, upon a door-step. The misery with them all was, clearly, that they sought to interfere, for good, in human matters, and had lost the power for ever.

Whether these creatures faded into mist, or mist enshrouded them, he could not tell. But they and their spirit voices faded together; and the light became as it had been when he walked home.

Scrooge closed the window, and examined the door by which the Ghost had entered. It was double-locked, as he had locked it with his own hands, and the bolts were undisturbed. He tried to say "Humbug!" but stopped at the first syllable. And being, from the emotion he had undergone, or the fatigues of the day, or his glimpse of the Invisible World, or the dull conversation of the Ghost, or the lateness of the hour, much in need of repose; went straight to bed, without undressing, and fell asleep upon the instant.

Phantoms

MONEY

Business! Mankind was my business. The common welfare was my business; charity, mercy, forbearance and benevolence, were, all, my business. The dealings of my trade were but a drop of water in the comprehensive ocean of my business!

Every year there is no shortage of memes tossed about on social media expressing some sort of variation on the cynical statement that "*A Christmas Carol* is the heartwarming tale of how rich people must be supernaturally terrorized into sharing." Whenever I see this sort of thing, I am sadly reminded of how many people have only seen the story on stage or screen and have never actually read the book. The tale was immediately adapted for the stage. In fact, there were twelve different theatrical productions running in England before the novel was a year in print, with only one of them sanctioned by Mr. Dickens. Most of the others highlighted the ghosts and flying scenery, and suffered from what one might call "coarse" acting. To date, there are at least 135 film adaptations. A few of these have merit. (I personally recommend the 1984 adaptation starring George C. Scott.) Too many of them, however, are merely parodies serving as a cheap vehicle for showcasing the acting talent of Mickey Mouse, Mr. Magoo, Kermit the Frog, and comedian Jim Carrey. (If you must watch any of these, see the frog.) These cartoonish and overly simplified adaptations have always threatened to obscure the real message of the book.

The trouble is scriptwriters all too often strip the story of the rich narrative sections where Dickens fully develops not just one, but several themes wound around the central character of Ebenezer Scrooge. These beautifully rendered passages are very much in keeping with Dickens' stated purpose as a writer: "to contribute...to the common stock of healthful cheerfulness and enjoyment." When they are deleted from the text, it turns the story into an oversimplified, cynical tale Dickens might call "a mole-eyed philosophy which loves darkness, and winks and scowls in the light." In other words, the drama is reduced to a contempt for the rich, which is not at all what Dickens wanted to say. If anything, he wanted to express the joy of the poor.

You may assume contempt for the rich is the joy of the poor, two sides of the same coin. But actually they are exact opposites. The sterling weight between rich and poor is inconsequential, because we are not talking about the physical world but the metaphysical. Remember, *A Christmas Carol* is a ghost story with vividly described scenes not unlike images from a certain magic lantern movie in which money is not given nearly as much weight as the intangible treasures of the heart—faith, family, friends—the things wise men consider the coin of true wealth. In the vivid descriptions of every street, every house, every room—wherever people come together in heart—there is such an abundance of these priceless treasures it is "impossible to add and count 'em up...The happiness is quite as great as if it cost a fortune."

With masterful manipulation of the English language, Dickens projects upon our imaginations a series of pictures in sharply contrasting light and shadow, illustrating how a bitterly cold and frozen alley can be turned into a winter playground, how a dusty warehouse is transformed into a beautiful ballroom, how the fire on a simple hearth glows to brighten the darkest night. Sick beds become cheerful, distant shores are brought close to home, struggling men are made patient in their greater hope. In scene after scene Dickens shows us wherever there is laid up treasures of the heart, poverty is made rich.

In his analysis of Dickens' life and work, British author G. K. Chesterton says that as a social reformer, Dickens sought to help the poor not by magnifying their misery but by describing their happiness, and men rushed to remove their sorrow. I have witnessed for myself how audience members are so moved by Dickens' story that following my performance, they are compelled to find a Bob Cratchit of their own, make his acquaintance, and purchase a proverbial coal scuttle to warm his home and office. Frustrated with the lack of an immediate opportunity to "do something," some people have pressed twenty-dollar bills into my hand and with tears in their eyes asked me to buy my own children whatever they would like for Christmas! This is a particularly awkward predicament for me because the purchase of the ticket to come see my show has amply provided for my children, yet the donor refuses to take the money back. Consequently, several years ago I began selecting a charity my audience members could support with their generous hearts.

The different projects are some of my favorite holiday memories. The first was a benefit performance in 2012 supporting children's programming at the International Storytelling Center in Jonesborough, Tennessee. Two years later I performed the show as a featured teller at the National Storytelling Festival. The festival audience was encouraged to purchase an extra storytelling recording when they shopped in the resource tent and drop it into a giant gift box by the cash register. These CDs were then shipped to US troops stationed overseas at Christmastime. The audience donated $1500 worth of recordings from more than a dozen different storytellers. Another year in my hometown, I offered a free digital download of the show to anyone who brought a non-perishable food item to the town square. I accepted all the donations for the local food bank dressed in my Dickens costume and standing by a long, black hearse on loan from a downtown funeral home. We stacked it full of food to help "bury hunger in Summerville." In other years audiences have donated funds for flood relief, hurricane relief, and youth programs. They have purchased toys and Christmas gifts for children with incarcerated parents.

The plight of homeless children was one of Dickens' most commonly recurring themes. A few years ago, with this fact in mind, I was approaching my 127th performance of *A Christmas Carol*. This was a big deal for me personally as it meant I would match Dickens in number of performances show for show. I decided to make it a bigger deal by promoting the performance as a benefit for "orphan relief." I am particularly proud of the Ebenezer Scrooge Adoption Fund, which was established in 2019 and makes no-interest loans to families seeking to adopt a child. I personally know two children whose adoptions were funded in part by these donations.

To date my audiences have donated over $25,000 to charity and I'm still counting, because a portion of the purchase price of this book is being donated to charity. All that money. All that love. Now that would make a good movie! Somebody should call the Hallmark Channel.

Mr. & Mrs. Fezziwig

STAVE TWO

THE FIRST OF THE THREE SPIRITS

When Scrooge awoke, it was so dark, that looking out of bed, he could scarcely distinguish the transparent window from the opaque walls of his chamber. He was endeavoring to pierce the darkness with his ferret eyes, when the chimes of a neighboring church struck the four quarters. So he listened for the hour.

To his great astonishment the heavy bell went on from six to seven, and from seven to eight, and regularly up to twelve; then stopped. Twelve! It was past two when he went to bed. The clock was wrong. An icicle must have got into the works. Twelve!

He touched the spring of his repeater, to correct this most preposterous clock. Its rapid little pulse beat twelve; and stopped.

"Why, it isn't possible," said Scrooge, "that I can have slept through a whole day and far into another night. It isn't possible that anything has happened to the sun, and this is twelve at noon!"

The idea being an alarming one, he scrambled out of bed, and groped his way to the window. He was obliged to rub the frost off with the sleeve of his dressing-gown before he could see anything; and could see very little then. All he could make out was, that it was still very foggy and extremely cold, and that there was no noise of people running to and fro, and making a great stir, as there unquestionably would have been if night had beaten off bright day, and taken possession of the world. This was a great relief, because "three days after sight of this First of Exchange pay to Mr. Ebenezer Scrooge or his order," and so forth, would have become a mere United States' security if there were no days to count by.

Scrooge went to bed again, and thought, and thought, and thought it over and over and over, and could make nothing of it. The more he thought, the more perplexed he was; and the more he endeavoured not to think, the more he thought. Marley's Ghost bothered him exceedingly. Every time he resolved within himself, after mature inquiry, that it was all a dream, his mind flew back again, like a strong spring released, to its first position, and presented the same problem to be worked all through, "Was it a dream or not?"

Scrooge lay in this state until the chimes had gone three quarters more, when he remembered, on a sudden, that the Ghost had warned him of a visitation when the bell tolled one. He resolved to lie awake until the hour was past; and, considering that he could no more go to sleep than go to Heaven, this was perhaps the wisest resolution in his power.

The quarter was so long, that he was more than once convinced he must have sunk into a doze unconsciously, and missed the clock. At length it broke upon his listening ear.

"Ding, dong!"

"A quarter past," said Scrooge, counting.

"Ding, dong!"

"Half past!" said Scrooge.

"Ding, dong!"

"A quarter to it," said Scrooge.

"Ding, dong!"

"The hour itself," said Scrooge, triumphantly, "and nothing else!"

He spoke before the hour bell sounded, which it now did with a deep, dull, hollow, melancholy One. Light flashed up in the room upon the instant, and the curtains of his bed were drawn.

The curtains of his bed were drawn aside, I tell you, by a hand. Not the curtains at his feet, nor the curtains at his back, but those to which his face was addressed. The curtains of his bed were drawn aside; and Scrooge, starting up into a half-recumbent attitude, found himself face to face with the unearthly visitor who drew them: as close to it as I am now to you, and I am standing in the spirit at your elbow.

It was a strange figure—like a child: yet not so like a child as like an old man, viewed through some supernatural medium, which gave him the appearance of having receded from the view, and being diminished to a child's proportions. Its hair, which hung about its neck and down its back, was white as if with age; and yet the face had not a wrinkle in it, and the tenderest bloom was on the skin. The arms were very long and muscular; the hands the same, as if its hold were of uncommon strength. Its legs and feet, most delicately formed, were, like those upper members, bare. It wore a tunic of the purest white; and round its waist was bound a lustrous belt, the sheen of which was beautiful. It held a branch of fresh green holly in its hand; and, in singular contradiction of that wintry emblem, had its dress trimmed with summer flowers. But the strangest thing about it was, that from the crown of its head there sprung a bright clear jet of light, by which all this was visible; and which was doubtless the occasion of its using, in its duller moments, a great extinguisher for a cap, which it now held under its arm.

Even this, though, when Scrooge looked at it with increasing steadiness, was not its strangest quality. For as its belt sparkled and glittered now in one part and now in another, and what was light one instant, at another time was dark, so the figure itself fluctuated in its distinctness: being now a thing with one arm, now with one leg, now with twenty legs, now a pair of legs without a head, now a head without a body: of which dissolving parts, no outline would be visible in the dense gloom wherein they melted away. And in the very wonder of this, it would be itself again; distinct and clear as ever.

"Are you the Spirit, sir, whose coming was foretold to me?" asked Scrooge.

"I am!"

The voice was soft and gentle. Singularly low, as if instead of being so close beside him, it were at a distance.

"Who, and what are you?" Scrooge demanded.

"I am the Ghost of Christmas Past."

"Long past?" inquired Scrooge: observant of its dwarfish stature.

"No. Your past."

Perhaps, Scrooge could not have told anybody why, if anybody could have asked him; but he had a special desire to see the Spirit in his cap; and begged him to be covered.

"What!" exclaimed the Ghost, "would you so soon put out, with worldly hands, the light I give? Is it not enough that you are one of those whose passions made this cap, and force me through whole trains of years to wear it low upon my brow!"

Scrooge reverently disclaimed all intention to offend, or any knowledge of having willfully "bonneted" the Spirit at any period of his life. He then made bold to inquire what business brought him there.

"Your welfare!" said the Ghost.

Scrooge expressed himself much obliged, but could not help thinking that a night of unbroken rest would have been more conducive to that end. The Spirit must have heard him thinking, for it said immediately:

"Your reclamation, then. Take heed!"

It put out its strong hand as it spoke, and clasped him gently by the arm.

"Rise! and walk with me!"

It would have been in vain for Scrooge to plead that the weather and the hour were not adapted to pedestrian purposes; that the bed was warm, and the thermometer a long way below freezing; that he was clad but lightly in his slippers, dressing-gown, and nightcap; and that he had a cold upon him at that time. The grasp, though gentle as a woman's hand, was not to be resisted. He rose: but finding that the Spirit made towards the window, clasped its robe in supplication.

"I am a mortal," Scrooge remonstrated, "and liable to fall."

"Bear but a touch of my hand there," said the Spirit, laying it upon his heart, "and you shall be upheld in more than this!"

LIGHT

It was a strange figure...But the strangest thing about it was, that from the crown of its head there sprung a bright clear jet of light.

I would happily perform *A Christmas Carol* year-round. It is the most popular story in my repertoire and consequently it is the most lucrative. I am thankful for the revenue. As the holiday carol says, "Praise the Lord for dark December! Fum! Fum! Fum!" However, Christmas comes but once a year and I must have performance material for the other eleven months on the calendar. Consequently, as I write this essay on light I am also conducting research on the great inventor Thomas Edison, the bringer of light. I hope a show about Edison will be popular with school children everywhere. Science, technology, engineering, math, and all of that. However, I will admit it isn't his scientific achievements so much as the character of Thomas Edison that fascinates me. His bright and shining personality simply could not—or perhaps it would be more correct to say would not—be extinguished. There was a certain impishness about Mr. Edison that contributed to his reputation as a wizard of technology.

This concept of an inextinguishable light radiating from a luminescent and impish personality is a recurring theme in *A Christmas Carol*. You might say it is Dickens' version of the Wagnerian "light motif." (Sorry, bad pun. I couldn't resist.) But seriously folks, Dickens references the same source material Richard Wagner used for his famous Ring Cycle operas. In Norse mythology, there is a Yule story of Baldr, the god of illumination, being killed by a dart which is fashioned from mistletoe by the trickster Loki. When Baldr is resurrected and light returns to Earth, his mother expresses her gratefulness by kissing any man who stands beneath the mistletoe. Contemporary to this Norse myth is the Celtic tradition of the Holly King who is a god of winter darkness. He is overcome each spring by the Oak King, who brings back the light of spring and summer. On the darkest day of the year, the ancient Celts would burn an oaken Yule log in anticipation of brighter days as they looked forward to the annual return of spring.

It is said that one of Dickens' goals was to revive an interest in these ancient Yule traditions that were in danger of being completely forgotten by the Victorians of his age. Consequently, the Ghosts of Christmases Past and Present with their mistletoe, holly, torch lights, and roaring fires are references to these old stories. These references not only renewed interest in the old customs, but also helped make a particularly English story more universal. Throughout the ages, cultures around the world have spun stories about characters known as "Bringers of Light." The Greek myth of Prometheus, the Inuit trickster Raven, and the Polynesian character of Maui, all come to mind. These various stories from around the globe seem to have a couple details in common. One, the light is always victorious. It may be dimmed or veiled for a time, but the dawn always breaks forth. Two, the character who brings the light is often a shapeshifter, a trickster, a playful, cheeky fellow. Dickens uses both of these ideas to great effect.

The light of memory, personified by the Ghost of Christmas Past, appears to Scrooge as some sort of flickering flame carrying a large candle snuffer for a hat. Upon his initial encounter with the ghost, Scrooge has a strong desire to see the flame "bonneted" but the spirit explains such a dimming would not only be cruel but counter-productive. Abandoning his effort to dim the Spirit's light, Scrooge follows the ghost through many scenes from times past and discovers with much delight several happy memories. The least of which is certainly not old Fezziwig, who radiates joy and mirth as he dances to the delight of everyone at the Christmas ball. Dickens notes that "a positive light seemed to issue from Fezziwig's calves. They shone in every part of the dance like moons." Whenever I quote this section of the tale during performances I must work hard to stifle laughter, because I have a vivid image of a particular Fezziwig who will forever be to me the very personification of what one might call a "luminary."

Several years ago I had the great pleasure of directing an amateur theatrical production of *A Christmas Carol* for a local church group. Not unlike Fezziwig's warehouse turned ballroom, the production had a limited budget. Nonetheless, we made up for any shortcomings with ample amounts of determination and good cheer. Every cast member served double duty as a member of the stage crew. If you were not delivering lines on the stage, then you were busily engaged behind the curtain shifting scenery, moving furniture, and organizing props, all the while listening for your cue, ready to drop whatever you were doing, and dash onto the stage just in the nick of time. Getting everything ready for the ballroom scene with "old Fezziwig looking on" presented a particular challenge. Every single cast member was responsible for delivering a prop to the stage. The list of required items included holiday garlands to hang from the rafters, chairs to be placed in various groupings, a table laden with platters of faux food, and a full-size china cabinet filled with plates, cups, and saucers. The actors had less than thirty seconds to carry all of this truck onto the stage, place it just so, and assume their places before the rise of the curtain. The only cast member who did not have something to carry, shift, move, or anchor was Old Fezziwig. His job was to stand before the curtain and stall for time with ad libs and general banter to keep the audience entertained during the scene change.

We had rehearsed and rehearsed and rehearsed, but this particular scene change never went well. Finally, it was dress rehearsal before a test audience. Being an amateur church group, we said a prayer and hoped for the best. When the big scene change came, Fezziwig stepped before the curtain and began his routine. "Pip, pip! Cheerio! Let's have these shutters up before a man can say 'Jack Robinson.' We'll want lots of room here.

Christmas, Ebenezer! Christmas, Dick! That's it boys, clear away, clear away!" All the while the audience could hear from behind the curtain what sounded like a herd of elephants moving the entire contents of Buckingham Palace onto the floor of the stage.

Finally, the curtain flew up to reveal...nothing. There had been a horrible traffic jam backstage resulting in a jumble of people, props, and Christmas decorations all piled on top of one another in the wings. There stood Fezziwig in the center of an empty stage and at a complete loss as to what should be done. I was sitting at the back of the auditorium, hiding behind the test audience, because I so feared some humiliating thing like this would happen. Fezziwig, with an expression of "What should I do?" on his face, took a quick look around trying to catch my eye. When I was nowhere to be seen, he hopped forward with a sort of jig step, struck a pose in the spotlight, looked directly at the audience, and sang out "ta-da!" There was not a single person in that house who was not fully aware of the fiasco.

Whether it was out of sympathy or amusement I cannot say, but the audience burst out with laughter and applause as Fezziwig just stood there, holding his pose for what seemed like the longest time, his face beaming as bright as a Christmas star. Finally, the rest of the cast arrived. "In they all came, one after another; some shyly (carrying holiday garlands), some boldly (with hammer and nails to hang them), some gracefully (with platters of faux food), some awkwardly (struggling at either end of a table), some pushing (chairs and children), some pulling (a full size china cabinet with cups and saucers rattling precariously): in they all came, anyhow and everyhow."

As I recall that scene even now, years later, I laugh until the tears stream down my cheeks. Just like the Ghost of Christmas Past who teaches Scrooge the same truth, Fezziwig, standing center stage all by himself with that great luminescent smile, taught me that nothing, NOTHING, will suppress the light that is the Spirit of Christmas. What is said of him in the novel is quite true: "The happiness he gives is quite as great as if it cost a fortune." God bless Old Fezziwig!

The Ghost of Christmas Present, like the great Oak King of Celtic lore, announces his arrival with such a bright light it illuminates every nook and cranny of Scrooge's dingy apartment and converts the dreary suite of rooms into a bright banquet hall, complete with a roaring hearth fire reminiscent of the old Yule log tradition. As Scrooge travels through the streets of London with the Ghost he observes that the source of this magical light is a torch emitting a curious sort of glittering luminescence that makes angry men quiet and rough fellows thoughtful. It also has the power to turn men of meager means into wealthy lords for the celebration of Christmas. Two outstanding examples of men so blessed are Scrooge's clerk, Bob Cratchit, and his nephew, Fred. Both characters generously share the warmth and good humor they have received from the Spirit of Christmas Present. It could be said they have the ability to "light up a room." Bob is a delight to his children, and Fred in particular is the very personification of the playful, cheeky fellow who is so often a bringer of light.

After visiting in these familiar homes, Scrooge is taken on a journey that stretches far and wide. He observes there is no room, no cell, no hovel, no heath, no lonely or forgotten place—no matter how dark—that can dim or extinguish the light brought by the Ghost of Christmas Present. However, as the twelve days of Christmas pass, the Ghost of Christmas Present grows old and weak. Instead of a Holly King bringing the darker nights of winter, Dickens employs the Ghost of Christmas Future, who casts a black shadow more terrifying than any Celtic deity of ancient times, and the narrative quickly becomes dark under his shadow.

In this cold shadow, Ebenezer Scrooge realizes just how awful the human existence would be without the bringers of light. Every street or house or room Scrooge peeks into displays a cynical, cold, mournful, melancholic, or hopeless scene. He begins to realize that not only does this Phantom of the Future cast a dark shadow, but also the merry fellows—Fezziwig, Bob Cratchit, his nephew Fred, the bringers of light—are very much subdued, if not entirely missing, from these gray and horrible pictures. Then at last, standing by the side of his own grave, Scrooge recognizes the terrible reality of Jacob Marley's words: "that no space of regret can make amends for one life's opportunities misused." Scrooge could have made a difference. He could have been a bringer of light in every single one of these situations, but instead he chose to love the darkness and remain in the shadows of cynicism and bitterness. In complete despair, Scrooge begs for a second chance and promises to live in the Past, and the Present, and the Future. In other words, he would like to live the remainder of his days "in light" of all he has learned.

Suddenly, like a star's ray piercing through the blackest night, it is Christmas Day! To employ a biblical phrase, Scrooge is immediately brought out of darkness and into the marvelous light. The change is very rapid, almost instantaneous, and Scrooge wonders if his experience is real. However, the reality is confirmed in two very familiar ways. First, the light of Christmas is inextinguishable. When the former lover of darkness flings open his window there is "no fog, no mist" but instead "golden sunlight" and "heavenly sky," and he finds the urge to laugh, shout, and dance as irrepressible as the light of day. Second, and even more glorious in my way of thinking, Scrooge becomes a shape-shifter, a trickster. Certainly not the man he used to be, he immediately begins his new career as a playful, cheeky fellow by surprising his nephew, playing a joke on Bob Cratchit, and joyfully shocking anyone who knew him in his former dark existence. He has become a "bringer of light"!

I began this essay with a reference to Thomas Edison. Sadly, Charles Dickens did not live long enough to witness the world premiere of the light bulb. Dying in 1870, he missed the wonderful event by less than a decade. On New Year's Eve in 1879, Edison updated the ancient tradition of casting a light on the darkest night of the year when he strung a wire of forty light bulbs along his driveway at Menlo Park, New Jersey. Thousands of people rode by in horse-drawn carriages to see this scientific wonder and marvel at the twinkling lights that seemed to magically illuminate the fresh, white snow on the ground. I'm sure Dickens would have been thrilled to see a tradition he helped preserve continue into the modern era. We should say a prayer of thanks for Dickens and Edison, bringers of light, every time we pile the family into the car to drive around town and practice the age-old custom of "Christmas light looking." To paraphrase an ancient hymn, "Praise the Lord for dark December! Vroom! Vroom! Vroom!"

As the words were spoken, they passed through the wall, and stood upon an open country road, with fields on either hand. The city had entirely vanished. Not a vestige of it was to be seen. The darkness and the mist had vanished with it, for it was a clear, cold, winter day, with snow upon the ground.

"Good Heaven!" said Scrooge, clasping his hands together, as he looked about him. "I was bred in this place. I was a boy here!"

The Spirit gazed upon him mildly. Its gentle touch, though it had been light and instantaneous, appeared still present to the old man's sense of feeling. He was conscious of a thousand odours floating in the air, each one connected with a thousand thoughts, and hopes, and joys, and cares long, long, forgotten!

"Your lip is trembling," said the Ghost. "And what is that upon your cheek?"

Scrooge muttered, with an unusual catching in his voice, that it was a pimple; and begged the Ghost to lead him where he would.

"You recollect the way?" inquired the Spirit.

"Remember it!" cried Scrooge with fervor—"I could walk it blindfold."

"Strange to have forgotten it for so many years!" observed the Ghost. "Let us go on."

They walked along the road; Scrooge recognizing every gate, and post, and tree; until a little market-town appeared in the distance, with its bridge, its church, and winding river. Some shaggy ponies now were seen trotting towards them with boys upon their backs, who called to other boys in country gigs and carts, driven by farmers. All these boys were in great spirits, and shouted to each other, until the broad fields were so full of merry music, that the crisp air laughed to hear it.

"These are but shadows of the things that have been," said the Ghost. "They have no consciousness of us."

The jocund travelers came on; and as they came, Scrooge knew and named them every one. Why was he rejoiced beyond all bounds to see them! Why did his cold eye glisten, and his heart leap up as they went past! Why was he filled with gladness when he heard them give each other Merry Christmas, as they parted at cross-roads and-bye ways, for their several homes! What was merry Christmas to Scrooge? Out upon merry Christmas! What good had it ever done to him?

"The school is not quite deserted," said the Ghost. "A solitary child, neglected by his friends, is left there still."

Scrooge said he knew it. And he sobbed.

They left the high-road, by a well remembered lane, and soon approached a mansion of dull red brick, with a little weathercock-surmounted cupola, on the roof, and a bell hanging in it. It was a large house, but one of broken fortunes; for the spacious offices were little used, their walls were damp and mossy, their windows broken, and their gates decayed. Fowls clucked and strutted in the stables; and the coach-houses and sheds were overrun with grass. Nor was it more retentive of its ancient state, within; for entering the dreary hall, and glancing through the open doors of many rooms, they found them poorly furnished, cold, and vast. There was an earthy savor in the air, a chilly bareness in the place, which associated itself somehow with too much getting up by candle-light, and not too much to eat.

They went, the Ghost and Scrooge, across the hall, to a door at the back of the house. It opened before them, and disclosed a long, bare, melancholy room, made barer still by lines of plain deal forms and desks. At one of these a lonely boy was reading near a feeble fire; and Scrooge sat down upon a form, and wept to see his poor forgotten self as he had used to be.

Not a latent echo in the house, not a squeak and scuffle from the mice behind the panelling, not a drip from the half-thawed water-spout in the dull yard behind, not a sigh among the leafless boughs of one despondent poplar, not the idle swinging of an empty store-house door, no, not a clicking in the fire, but fell upon the heart of Scrooge with softening influence, and gave a freer passage to his tears.

The Spirit touched him on the arm, and pointed to his younger self, intent upon his reading. Suddenly a man, in foreign garments: wonderfully real and distinct to look at: stood outside the window, with an axe stuck in his belt, and leading an ass laden with wood by the bridle.

"Why, it's Ali Baba!" Scrooge exclaimed in ecstasy. "It's dear old honest Ali Baba! Yes, yes, I know! One Christmas time, when yonder solitary child was left here all alone, he did come, for the first time, just like that. Poor boy! And Valentine," said Scrooge, "and his wild brother, Orson; there they go! And what's his name, who was put down in his drawers, asleep, at the Gate of Damascus; don't you see him! And the Sultan's Groom turned upside-down by the Genii; there he is upon his head! Serve him right. I'm glad of it. What business had he to be married to the Princess!"

To hear Scrooge expending all the earnestness of his nature on such subjects, in a most extraordinary voice between laughing and crying; and to see his heightened and excited face; would have been a surprise to his business friends in the city, indeed.

"There's the Parrot!" cried Scrooge. "Green body and yellow tail, with a thing like a lettuce growing out of the top of his head; there he is! Poor Robin Crusoe, he called him, when he came home again after sailing round the island.

'Poor Robin Crusoe, where have you been, Robin Crusoe?'
The man thought he was dreaming, but he wasn't. It was
the Parrot, you know. There goes Friday, running for his
life to the little creek! Halloa! Hoop! Halloo!"

Then, with a rapidity of transition very foreign to his
usual character, he said, in pity for his former self, "Poor
boy!" and cried again.

"I wish," Scrooge muttered, putting his hand in his
pocket, and looking about him, after drying his eyes with
his cuff: "but it's too late now."

"What is the matter?" asked the Spirit.

"Nothing," said Scrooge. "Nothing. There was a boy
singing a Christmas Carol at my door last night. I should
like to have given him something: that's all."

The Ghost smiled thoughtfully, and waved its hand:
saying as it did so, "Let us see another Christmas!"

Scrooge's former self grew larger at the words, and the
room became a little darker and more dirty. The panels
shrunk, the windows cracked; fragments of plaster fell out
of the ceiling, and the naked laths were shown instead:
but how all this was brought about, Scrooge knew no more
than you do. He only knew that it was quite correct; that
everything had happened so; that there he was, alone
again, when all the other boys had gone home for the jolly
holidays.

He was not reading now, but walking up and down
despairingly. Scrooge looked at the Ghost, and with a

mournful shaking of his head, glanced anxiously towards the door.

It opened; and a little girl, much younger than the boy, came darting in, and putting her arms about his neck, and often kissing him, addressed him as her "Dear, dear brother."

"I have come to bring you home, dear brother!" said the child, clapping her tiny hands, and bending down to laugh. "To bring you home, home, home!"

"Home, little Fan?" returned the boy.

"Yes!" said the child, brimful of glee, "Home, for good and all. Home, for ever and ever. Father is so much kinder than he used to be, that home's like Heaven! He spoke so gently to me one dear night when I was going to bed, that I was not afraid to ask him once more if you might come home; and he said Yes, you should; and sent me in a coach to bring you. And you're to be a man!" said the child, opening her eyes, "and are never to come back here; but first, we're to be together all the Christmas long, and have the merriest time in all the world."

"You are quite a woman, little Fan!" exclaimed the boy.

She clapped her hands and laughed, and tried to touch his head; but being too little, laughed again, and stood on tiptoe to embrace him. Then she began to drag him, in her childish eagerness, towards the door; and he, nothing loth to go, accompanied her.

A terrible voice in the hall cried, "Bring down Master Scrooge's box, there!" and in the hall appeared the schoolmaster himself, who glared on Master Scrooge with a ferocious condescension, and threw him into a dreadful state of mind by shaking hands with him. He then conveyed him and his sister into the veriest old well of a shivering best parlour that ever was seen, where the maps upon the wall, and the celestial and terrestrial globes in the windows, were waxy with cold. Here he produced a decanter of curiously light wine, and a block of curiously heavy cake, and administered installments of those dainties to the young people: at the same time, sending out a meagre servant to offer a glass of "something" to the postboy, who answered that he thanked the gentleman, but if it was the same tap as he had tasted before, he had rather not. Master Scrooge's trunk being by this time tied on to the top of the chaise, the children bade the schoolmaster good-bye right willingly; and getting into it, drove gaily down the garden-sweep: the quick wheels dashing the hoar-frost and snow from off the dark leaves of the evergreens like spray.

"Always a delicate creature, whom a breath might have withered," said the Ghost. "But she had a large heart!"

"So she had," cried Scrooge. "You're right. I'll not gainsay it, Spirit. God forbid!"

"She died a woman," said the Ghost," and had, as I think, children."

"One child," Scrooge returned.

"True," said the Ghost. "Your nephew!"

Scrooge seemed uneasy in his mind; and answered briefly, "Yes."

Although they had but that moment left the school behind them, they were now in the busy thoroughfares of a city, where shadowy passengers passed and repassed; where shadowy carts and coaches battled for the way, and all the strife and tumult of a real city were. It was made plain enough, by the dressing of the shops, that here too it was Christmas time again; but it was evening, and the streets were lighted up.

The Ghost stopped at a certain warehouse door, and asked Scrooge if he knew it.

"Know it!" said Scrooge. "Was I apprenticed here!"

They went in. At sight of an old gentleman in a Welch wig, sitting behind such a high desk, that if he had been two inches taller he must have knocked his head against the ceiling, Scrooge cried in great excitement:

"Why, it's old Fezziwig! Bless his heart; it's Fezziwig alive again!"

Old Fezziwig laid down his pen and looked up at the clock, which pointed to the hour of seven. He rubbed his hands; adjusted his capacious waistcoat; laughed all over himself, from his shoes to his organ of benevolence; and called out in a comfortable, oily, rich, fat, jovial voice:

"Yo ho, there! Ebenezer! Dick!"

Scrooge's former self, now grown a young man, came briskly in, accompanied by his fellow-'prentice.

"Dick Wilkins, to be sure!" said Scrooge to the Ghost. "Bless me, yes. There he is. He was very much attached to me, was Dick. Poor Dick! Dear, dear!"

"Yo ho, my boys!" said Fezziwig. "No more work to-night. Christmas Eve, Dick. Christmas, Ebenezer! Let's have the shutters up," cried old Fezziwig, with a sharp clap of his hands, "before a man can say, Jack Robinson!"

You wouldn't believe how those two fellows went at it! They charged into the street with the shutters—one, two, three—had 'em up in their places—four, five, six—barred 'em and pinned 'em—seven, eight, nine—and came back before you could have got to twelve, panting like race-horses.

"Hilli-ho!" cried old Fezziwig, skipping down from the high desk, with wonderful agility. "Clear away, my lads, and let's have lots of room here! Hilli-ho, Dick! Chirrup, Ebenezer!"

Clear away! There was nothing they wouldn't have cleared away, or couldn't have cleared away, with old Fezziwig looking on. It was done in a minute. Every movable was packed off, as if it were dismissed from public life for evermore; the floor was swept and watered, the lamps were trimmed, fuel was heaped upon the fire; and the warehouse was as snug, and warm, and dry, and bright a ball-room, as you would desire to see upon a winter's night.

In came a fiddler with a music-book, and went up to the lofty desk, and made an orchestra of it, and tuned like fifty stomach-aches. In came Mrs. Fezziwig, one vast substantial smile. In came the three Miss Fezziwigs, beaming and lovable. In came the six young followers whose hearts they broke. In came all the young men and women employed in the business. In came the housemaid, with her cousin, the baker. In came the cook, with her brother's particular friend, the milkman. In came the boy from over the way, who was suspected of not having board enough from his master; trying to hide himself behind the girl from next door but one, who was proved to have had her ears pulled by her Mistress. In they all came, one after another; some shyly, some boldly, some gracefully, some awkwardly, some pushing, some pulling; in they all came, anyhow and everyhow. Away they all went, twenty couple at once, hands half round and back again the other way; down the middle and up again; round and round in various stages of affectionate grouping; old top couple always turning up in the wrong place; new top couple starting off again, as soon as they got there; all top couples at last, and not a bottom one to help them. When this result was brought about, old Fezziwig, clapping his hands to stop the dance, cried out, "Well done!" and the fiddler plunged his hot face into a pot of porter, especially provided for that purpose. But scorning rest upon his reappearance, he instantly began again, though there were no dancers yet, as if the other fiddler had been carried home, exhausted, on a shutter; and he were a bran-new man resolved to beat him out of sight, or perish.

There were more dances, and there were forfeits, and more dances, and there was cake, and there was negus, and there was a great piece of Cold Roast, and there was a great piece of Cold Boiled, and there were mince-pies, and plenty of beer. But the great effect of the evening came after the Roast and Boiled, when the fiddler (an artful dog, mind! The sort of man who knew his business better than you or I could have told it him!) struck up "Sir Roger de Coverley." Then old Fezziwig stood out to dance with Mrs. Fezziwig. Top couple too; with a good stiff piece of work cut out for them; three or four and twenty pair of partners; people who were not to be trifled with; people who would dance, and had no notion of walking.

But if they had been twice as many: ah, four times: old Fezziwig would have been a match for them, and so would Mrs. Fezziwig. As to her, she was worthy to be his partner in every sense of the term. If that's not high praise, tell me higher, and I'll use it. A positive light appeared to issue from Fezziwig's calves. They shone in every part of the dance like moons. You couldn't have predicted, at any given time, what would become of 'em next. And when old Fezziwig and Mrs. Fezziwig had gone all through the dance; advance and retire, hold hands with your partner; bow and curtsey; corkscrew; thread-the-needle, and back again to your place; Fezziwig "cut"—cut so deftly, that he appeared to wink with his legs, and came upon his feet again without a stagger.

When the clock struck eleven, this domestic ball broke up. Mr. and Mrs. Fezziwig took their stations, one on either side the door, and shaking hands with every person individually as he or she went out, wished him or her a Merry Christmas. When everybody had retired but the two 'prentices, they did the same to them; and thus the cheerful voices died away, and the lads were left to their beds; which were under a counter in the back-shop.

During the whole of this time, Scrooge had acted like a man out of his wits. His heart and soul were in the scene, and with his former self. He corroborated everything, remembered everything, enjoyed everything, and underwent the strangest agitation. It was not until now, when the bright faces of his former self and Dick were turned from them, that he remembered the Ghost, and became conscious that it was looking full upon him, while the light upon its head burnt very clear.

"A small matter," said the Ghost, "to make these silly folks so full of gratitude."

"Small!" echoed Scrooge.

The Spirit signed to him to listen to the two apprentices, who were pouring out their hearts in praise of Fezziwig: and when he had done so, said,

"Why! Is it not? he has spent but a few pounds of your mortal money: three or four, perhaps. Is that so much that he deserves this praise?"

"It isn't that," said Scrooge, heated by the remark, and speaking unconsciously like his former, not his latter, self.

"It isn't that, Spirit, He has the power to render us happy or unhappy; to make our service light or burdensome; a pleasure or a toil. Say that his power lies in words and looks; in things so slight and insignificant that it is impossible to add and count 'em up: what then? The happiness he gives, is quite as great as if it cost a fortune."

He felt the Spirit's glance, and stopped.

"What is the matter?" asked the Ghost.

"Nothing particular," said Scrooge.

"Something, I think?" the Ghost insisted.

"No," said Scrooge, "No. I should like to be able to say a word or two to my clerk just now! That's all."

His former self turned down the lamps as he gave utterance to the wish; and Scrooge and the Ghost again stood side by side in the open air.

"My time grows short," observed the Spirit. "Quick!"

This was not addressed to Scrooge, or to any one whom he could see, but it produced an immediate effect. For again Scrooge saw himself. He was older now; a man in the prime of life. His face had not the harsh and rigid lines of later years; but it had begun to wear the signs of care and avarice. There was an eager, greedy, restless motion in the eye, which showed the passion that had taken root, and where the shadow of the growing tree would fall.

He was not alone, but sat by the side of a fair young girl in a mourning-dress: in whose eyes there were tears, which sparkled in the light that shone out of the Ghost of Christmas Past.

"It matters little," she said, softly. "To you, very little. Another idol has displaced me; and if it can cheer and comfort you in time to come, as I would have tried to do, I have no just cause to grieve."

"What Idol has displaced you?" he rejoined.

"A golden one."

"This is the even-handed dealing of the world!" he said. "There is nothing on which it is so hard as poverty; and there is nothing it professes to condemn with such severity as the pursuit of wealth!"

"You fear the world too much," she answered, gently. "All your other hopes have merged into the hope of being beyond the chance of its sordid reproach. I have seen your nobler aspirations fall off one by one, until the master-passion, Gain, engrosses you. Have I not?"

"What then?" he retorted. "Even if I have grown so much wiser, what then? I am not changed towards you."

She shook her head.

"Am I?"

"Our contract is an old one. It was made when we were both poor and content to be so, until, in good season, we could improve our worldly fortune by our patient industry. You are changed. When it was made, you were another man."

"I was a boy," he said impatiently.

"Your own feeling tells you that you were not what you are," she returned. "I am. That which promised happiness when we were one in heart, is fraught with misery now that we are two. How often and how keenly I have thought of this, I will not say. It is enough that I have thought of it, and can release you."

"Have I ever sought release?"

"In words. No. Never."

"In what, then?"

"In a changed nature; in an altered spirit; in another atmosphere of life; another Hope as its great end. In everything that made my love of any worth or value in your sight. If this had never been between us," said the girl, looking mildly, but with steadiness, upon him; "tell me, would you seek me out and try to win me now? Ah, no!"

He seemed to yield to the justice of this supposition, in spite of himself. But he said, with a struggle, "You think not."

"I would gladly think otherwise if I could," she answered, "Heaven knows! When I have learned a Truth like this, I know how strong and irresistible it must be. But if you were free to-day, to-morrow, yesterday, can even I believe that you would choose a dower-less girl—you who, in your very confidence with her, weigh everything by Gain: or, choosing her, if for a moment you were false enough to your one guiding principle to do so, do I not know that your repentance and regret would surely follow? I do; and I release you. With a full heart, for the love of him you once were."

He was about to speak; but with her head turned from him, she resumed.

"You may—the memory of what is past half makes me hope you will—have pain in this. A very, very brief time, and you will dismiss the recollection of it, gladly, as an unprofitable dream, from which it happened well that you awoke. May you be happy in the life you have chosen!"

She left him; and they parted.

"Spirit!" said Scrooge, "show me no more! Conduct me home. Why do you delight to torture me?"

"One shadow more!" exclaimed the Ghost.

"No more!" cried Scrooge. "No more. I don't wish to see it. Show me no more!"

But the relentless Ghost pinioned him in both his arms, and forced him to observe what happened next.

They were in another scene and place: a room, not very large or handsome, but full of comfort. Near to the winter fire sat a beautiful young girl, so like the last that Scrooge believed it was the same, until he saw her, now a comely matron, sitting opposite her daughter. The noise in this room was perfectly tumultuous, for there were more children there, than Scrooge in his agitated state of mind could count; and, unlike the celebrated herd in the poem, they were not forty children conducting themselves like one, but every child was conducting itself like forty. The consequences were uproarious beyond belief; but no one seemed to care; on the contrary, the mother and daughter laughed heartily, and enjoyed it very much; and the latter, soon beginning to mingle in the sports, got pillaged by the young brigands most ruthlessly. What would I not have

given to be one of them! Though I never could have been
so rude, no, no! I wouldn't for the wealth of all the world
have crushed that braided hair, and torn it down; and for
the precious little shoe, I wouldn't have plucked it off, God
bless my soul! to save my life. As to measuring her waist in
sport, as they did, bold young brood, I couldn't have done
it; I should have expected my arm to have grown round it
for a punishment, and never come straight again. And yet
I should have dearly liked, I own, to have touched her lips;
to have questioned her, that she might have opened them;
to have looked upon the lashes of her downcast eyes, and
never raised a blush; to have let loose waves of hair, an
inch of which would be a keepsake beyond price: in short,
I should have liked, I do confess, to have had the lightest
license of a child, and yet been man enough to know its
value.

But now a knocking at the door was heard, and such
a rush immediately ensued that she with laughing face
and plundered dress was borne towards it the centre of
a flushed and boisterous group, just in time to greet the
father, who, came home attended by a man laden with
Christmas toys and presents. Then the shouting and the
struggling, and the onslaught that was made on the de-
fenseless porter! The scaling him, with chairs for ladders,
to dive into his pockets, despoil him of brown-paper par-
cels, hold on tight by his cravat, hug him round the neck,
pommel his back, and kick his legs in irrepressible affection! The shouts of wonder and delight with which the

development of every package was received! The terrible announcement that the baby had been taken in the act of putting a doll's frying-pan into his mouth, and was more than suspected of having swallowed a fictitious turkey, glued on a wooden platter! The immense relief of finding this a false alarm! The joy, and gratitude, and ecstasy! They are all indescribable alike. It is enough that by degrees the children and their emotions got out of the parlor and by one stair at a time, up to the top of the house; where they went to bed, and so subsided.

And now Scrooge looked on more attentively than ever, when the master of the house, having his daughter leaning fondly on him, sat down with her and her mother at his own fireside; and when he thought that such another creature, quite as graceful and as full of promise, might have called him father, and been a spring-time in the haggard winter of his life, his sight grew very dim indeed.

"Belle," said the husband, turning to his wife with a smile, "I saw an old friend of yours this afternoon."

"Who was it?"

"Guess!"

"How can I? Tut, don't I know," she added in the same breath, laughing as he laughed. "Mr. Scrooge."

"Mr. Scrooge it was. I passed his office window; and as it was not shut up, and he had a candle inside, I could scarcely help seeing him. His partner lies upon the point of death, I hear; and there he sat alone. Quite alone in the world, I do believe."

"Spirit!" said Scrooge in a broken voice, "remove me from this place."

"I told you these were shadows of the things that have been," said the Ghost. "That they are what they are, do not blame me!"

"Remove me!" Scrooge exclaimed. "I cannot bear it!"

He turned upon the Ghost, and seeing that it looked upon him with a face, in which in some strange way there were fragments of all the faces it had shown him, wrestled with it.

"Leave me! Take me back. Haunt me no longer!"

In the struggle, if that can be called a struggle in which the Ghost with no visible resistance on its own part was undisturbed by any effort of its adversary, Scrooge observed that its light was burning high and bright; and dimly connecting that with its influence over him, he seized the extinguisher-cap, and by a sudden action pressed it down upon its head.

The Spirit dropped beneath it, so that the extinguisher covered its whole form; but though Scrooge pressed it down with all his force, he could not hide the light: which streamed from under it, in an unbroken flood upon the ground.

He was conscious of being exhausted, and overcome by an irresistible drowsiness; and, further, of being in his own bedroom. He gave the cap a parting squeeze, in which his hand relaxed; and had barely time to reel to bed, before he sank into a heavy sleep.

Scrooge Extinguishes the
Ghost of Christmas Past

CHILDREN

I should have liked, I do confess, to have the lightest license of a child, and yet been man enough to know its value.

I am of the firm opinion that any setting or situation can be improved with the addition of children. Without them the world would be appreciably more gray and ordinary. Granted, they are not intellectually stunning, physically strong, or beautifully graceful; but these are not the great contributions that children make to society. The child's gift to the world is their joy and spontaneity. There is nothing I like better than to see the change of atmosphere that is so instantly achieved by the antics of a child.

A number of years ago I was booked to perform *A Christmas Carol* at the River's Edge Restaurant in Cheraw, South Carolina. The establishment happens to be run by a Mennonite family. The Mennonite community is known for its sobriety and seriousness. This is most noticeable in choice of dress, where the rule of thumb is plain, not fancy. In a Mennonite worship service the congregational singing is a cappella, which means sung without musical accompaniment. Church buildings are functional and unadorned. It is a simple and straightforward expression of the Christian faith. My description of the Mennonite culture is not critical, it is merely my observation that it greatly contrasts with the highly decorated and flourished Anglican tradition of Dickens. Consequently, when I arrived at the Mennonite restaurant in full Victorian costume, my top hat and tails were quite the contrast to the simple dress of the folks making the food and preparing the dining room for my show.

Another distinction of Mennonite culture is the emphasis on family. Children are not segregated from the adults, they participate in every activity. When I arrived at the restaurant well ahead of showtime, there were many young people working. Several teenagers were helping out in the kitchen while younger children laid out silverware, arranged chairs, and made sure the candle on each table was lit and burning brightly. The teenagers in the kitchen sang Christmas carols as they worked. The a cappella singing with its beautiful harmonies made for a joyous and merry atmosphere, and the workers were planning to sing a few selections as pre-show entertainment for the restaurant patrons. Everything was ready with time to spare.

Checking my watch, I stepped out onto the sidewalk in front of the restaurant to greet patrons as they began to arrive. It wasn't long before several of the young people joined me. I very quickly found myself engaged in conversation with a group of boys ranging in age from seventeen down to seven. Some of the older boys told me about their apprenticeships with local craftsmen. Like their fathers and grandfathers, they were learning to be farmers, metal machinists, and carpenters. The middle boys told me all about their school exploits and how they had played a softball game that afternoon at recess. Soon they were all bragging about who was the fastest runner or the best batter. The youngest fellow, the seven-year-old, stood listening to the big boys talk about their work or their exploits on the ballfield. I didn't realize he was desperate to measure up until he turned to me, jerked a thumb in the general direction of a tall lamppost on the sidewalk, and exclaimed, "I can climb that pole right there." Before I could say a word or anybody could stop him, he was halfway up the ten-foot post. As I watched in amazement, he shinnied to the top and perched on the globe like a little bird!

About that time, the first restaurant patrons began to arrive and the older boys went back inside to resume their duties. My lamppost climber just stayed atop the pole. Dressed in black pants, high top shoes, and a plain-colored shirt, he looked every bit the part of a Dickens character, and there I was standing beneath him in my Victorian costume. As people came down the sidewalk or crossed the street and approached the restaurant, I tipped my hat to them and they smiled. Then from high above a child's voice called out "Merry Christmas!" Folks stopped and looked up to see a rosy-cheeked boy waving happily. I said "That's Tiny Tim. He's very excited to be here. Practically over the moon, you might say." Smiles changeed to full laughter as the restaurant patrons opened the door and the sounds of the teenagers' singing spilled out onto the sidewalk. The carol singing was nice, but the lamppost boy was an especially fun touch!

I love the spontaneity of children. They see an opportunity for mirth and they take it. No over-thinking. As the French might say, "Joie de Vivre!" Charles Dickens valued this quality as well. He once wrote in his magazine *Household Words*, "If we can only preserve ourselves from growing up, we shall never grow old, and the young may love us to the last. Not to be too wise, not to be too stately, not to be too rough with innocent fancies, or to treat them with too much lightness—which is as bad—are points to be remembered that may do us all good in our years to come."

Michael Patrick Hearn, editor of *The Annotated Christmas Carol*, notes that Dickens reinforces this idea by structuring his holiday story like a fairy tale. Early in the narrative he employs the classic phrase "once upon a time." Then the ghost of Jacob Marley suddenly appears, much like a fairy godmother, albeit a good bit more frightening. Next, Scrooge must experience three trials just like a hero in a folktale. And finally, Dickens concludes the story "happily ever after" with the more Christmassy "God Bless Us, Every One!" Hearn goes on to say Dickens also employs a good bit of personification in his story. Much like the fairytale author Hans Christian Andersen, he gives inanimate objects life by describing an iron bell with teeth, a house that plays hide-and-seek, Spanish onions that wink, and French plums that blush. "No one was more intensely fond than Dickens of old nursery tales," wrote John Forster, Dickens publisher and official biographer, "and he had a secret delight in feeling that he was here only giving them a higher form."

For those who have grown up too much and cannot find the pathway back to a more childlike approach to life, Dickens provides a model in the character development of Ebenezer Scrooge. In the beginning of the novel, Scrooge scorns the little boy who bends down at his office door to sing a carol through the keyhole. What stuff and nonsense! But later with the Ghost of Christmas Past, he is moved to tears as he views scenes from his own boyhood. He is especially elated to recall the characters from the stories he read as a child, remembering their antics and the resulting consequences. It is interesting to note most of these stories, in one way or another, employ "what one might call fancy" to teach lessons of fairness, goodwill, and generosity. Perhaps Dickens is saying the stories and fairy tales we hear or read as children tend to preach to us our whole lives. At any rate, we observe Scrooge growing ever more young at heart. With the Ghost of Christmas Present, he begs like a school boy to stay longer at Fred's Christmas party. After his time with the Ghost of Christmas Future, his transformation is complete and he happily declares himself to be a baby. It's as if Scrooge has aged backwards.

I think that is what Christmas time does for many of us adults. We are all of a sudden quite young again. We can laugh and sing and dance and skip and play. "For it is good to be children sometimes and never better than at Christmas when it's mighty Founder was a child himself." So haul out the holly, put up the tree, or, if nothing else, go shinny up a lamppost!

The Second of Three Spirits

STAVE THREE

THE SECOND OF THE THREE SPIRITS

Awaking in the middle of a prodigiously tough snore, and sitting up in bed to get his thoughts together, Scrooge had no occasion to be told that the bell was again upon the stroke of One. He felt that he was restored to consciousness in the right nick of time, for the especial purpose of holding a conference with the second messenger despatched to him through Jacob Marley's intervention. But finding that he turned uncomfortably cold when he began to wonder which of his curtains this new specter would draw back, he put them every one aside with his own hands; and lying down again, established a sharp look-out all round the bed. For he wished to challenge the Spirit on the moment of its appearance, and did not wish to be taken by surprise and made nervous.

Gentlemen of the free-and-easy sort, who plume themselves on being acquainted with a move or two, and being usually equal to the time-of-day, express the wide range of their capacity for adventure by observing that they are good for anything from pitch-and-toss to manslaughter; between which opposite extremes, no doubt, there lies a tolerably wide and comprehensive range of subjects. Without venturing for Scrooge quite as hardily as this, I don't mind calling on you to believe that he was ready for a good broad field of strange appearances, and that nothing between a baby and a rhinoceros would have astonished him very much.

Now, being prepared for almost anything, he was not by any means prepared for nothing; and, consequently, when the Bell struck One, and no shape appeared, he was taken with a violent fit of trembling. Five minutes, ten minutes, a quarter of an hour went by, yet nothing came. All this time, he lay upon his bed, the very core and centre of a blaze of ruddy light, which streamed upon it when the clock proclaimed the hour; and which being only light, was more alarming than a dozen ghosts, as he was powerless to make out what it meant, or would be at; and was sometimes apprehensive that he might be at that very moment an interesting case of spontaneous combustion, without having the consolation of knowing it. At last, however, he began to think—as you or I would have thought at first; for it is always the person not in the predicament who knows what ought to have been done in it, and would unquestionably have done it too—at last, I say, he began to think that the source and secret of this ghostly light might be in the adjoining room: from whence, on further tracing it, it seemed to shine. This idea taking full possession of his mind, he got up softly and shuffled in his slippers to the door.

The moment Scrooge's hand was on the lock, a strange voice called him by his name, and bade him enter. He obeyed.

It was his own room. There was no doubt about that. But it had undergone a surprising transformation. The walls and ceiling were so hung with living green, that it looked a perfect grove, from every part of which, bright gleaming berries glistened. The crisp leaves of holly, mistletoe, and ivy reflected back the light, as if so many little mirrors had been scattered there; and such a mighty blaze went roaring up the chimney, as that dull petrifaction of a hearth had never known in Scrooge's time, or Marley's, or for many and many a winter season gone. Heaped up upon the floor, to form a kind of throne, were turkeys, geese, game, poultry, brawn, great joints of meat, sucking-pigs, long wreaths of sausages, mince-pies, plum-puddings, barrels of oysters, red-hot chestnuts, cherry-cheeked apples, juicy oranges, luscious pears, immense twelfth-cakes, and seething bowls of punch, that made the chamber dim with their delicious steam. In easy state upon this couch, there sat a jolly Giant, glorious to see; who bore a glowing torch, in shape not unlike Plenty's horn, and held it up, high up, to shed its light on Scrooge, as he came peeping round the door.

"Come in!" exclaimed the Ghost. "Come in! and know me better, man!"

Scrooge entered timidly, and hung his head before this Spirit. He was not the dogged Scrooge he had been; and though its eyes were clear and kind, he did not like to meet them.

"I am the Ghost of Christmas Present," said the Spirit. "Look upon me!"

Scrooge reverently did so. It was clothed in one simple deep green robe, or mantle, bordered with white fur. This garment hung so loosely on the figure, that its capacious breast was bare, as if disdaining to be warded or concealed by any artifice. Its feet, observable beneath the ample folds of the garment, were also bare; and on its head it wore no other covering than a holly wreath set here and there with shining icicles. Its dark brown curls were long and free: free as its genial face, its sparkling eye, its open hand, its cheery voice, its unconstrained demeanor, and its joyful air. Girded round its middle was an antique scabbard; but no sword was in it, and the ancient sheath was eaten up with rust.

"You have never seen the like of me before!" exclaimed the Spirit.

"Never," Scrooge made answer to it.

"Have never walked forth with the younger members of my family; meaning (for I am very young) my elder brothers born in these later years?" pursued the Phantom.

"I don't think I have," said Scrooge. "I am afraid I have not. Have you had many brothers, Spirit?"

"More than eighteen hundred," said the Ghost.

"A tremendous family to provide for!" muttered Scrooge.

The Ghost of Christmas Present rose.

"Spirit," said Scrooge submissively, "conduct me where you will. I went forth last night on compulsion, and I learnt a lesson which is working now. To-night, if you have aught to teach me, let me profit by it."

"Touch my robe!"

Scrooge did as he was told, and held it fast.

Holly, mistletoe, red berries, ivy, turkeys, geese, game, poultry, brawn, meat, pigs, sausages, oysters, pies, puddings, fruit, and punch, all vanished instantly. So did the room, the fire, the ruddy glow, the hour of night, and they stood in the city streets on Christmas morning, where (for the weather was severe) the people made a rough, but brisk and not unpleasant kind of music, in scraping the snow from the pavement in front of their dwellings, and from the tops of their houses: whence it was mad delight to the boys to see it come plumping down into the road below, and splitting into artificial little snow-storms.

The house fronts looked black enough, and the windows blacker, contrasting with the smooth white sheet of snow upon the roofs, and with the dirtier snow upon the ground; which last deposit had been ploughed up in deep furrows by the heavy wheels of carts and wagons; furrows that crossed and re-crossed each other hundreds of times where the great streets branched off, and made intricate channels, hard to trace, in the thick yellow mud and icy water. The sky was gloomy, and the shortest streets were choked up with a dingy mist, half thawed half frozen, whose heavier particles descended in a shower of sooty atoms, as if all the chimneys in Great Britain had, by one consent, caught fire, and were blazing away to their dear hearts' content. There was nothing very cheerful in the climate or the town, and yet was there an air of cheerfulness abroad that the clearest summer air and brightest summer sun might have endeavored to diffuse in vain.

For the people who were shoveling away on the housetops were jovial and full of glee; calling out to one another from the parapets, and now and then exchanging a facetious snowball—better-natured missile far than many a wordy jest—laughing heartily if it went right, and not less heartily if it went wrong. The poulterers' shops were still half open, and the fruiterers' were radiant in their glory. There were great, round, pot-bellied baskets of chestnuts, shaped like the waistcoats of jolly old gentlemen lolling at the doors, and tumbling out into the street in their apoplectic opulence. There were ruddy, brown-faced, broad-girthed Spanish Onions, shining in the fatness of their growth like Spanish Friars; and winking from their shelves in wanton slyness at the girls as they went by, and glanced demurely at the hung-up mistletoe. There were pears and apples, clustered high in blooming pyramids; there were bunches of grapes, made, in the shopkeepers' benevolence, to dangle from conspicuous hooks, that people's mouths might water gratis as they passed; there were piles of filberts, mossy and brown, recalling, in their fragrance, ancient walks among the woods, and pleasant shufflings ankle deep through withered leaves, there were Norfolk Biffins, squab and swarthy, setting off the yellow of the oranges and lemons, and, in the great compactness of their juicy persons, urgently entreating and beseeching to be carried home in paper bags and eaten after dinner. The very gold and silver fish, set forth among these choice fruits in a bowl, though members of a dull and stagnant-blooded race, appeared to know that there was something going on; and, to a fish, went gasping round and round their little world in slow and passionless excitement.

The Grocers'! oh the Grocers'! nearly closed, with perhaps two shutters down, or one; but through those gaps such glimpses! It was not alone that the scales descending on the counter made a merry sound, or that the twine and roller parted company so briskly, or that the canisters were rattled up and down like juggling tricks, or even that the blended scents of tea and coffee were so grateful to the nose, or even that the raisins were so plentiful and rare, the almonds so extremely white, the sticks of cinnamon so long and straight, the other spices so delicious, the candied fruits so caked and spotted with molten sugar as to make the coldest lookers-on feel faint and subsequently bilious. Nor was it that the figs were moist and pulpy, or that the French plums blushed in modest tartness from their highly-decorated boxes, or that everything was good to eat and in its Christmas dress: but the customers were all so hurried and so eager in the hopeful promise of the day, that they tumbled up against each other at the door, clashing their wicker baskets wildly, and left their purchases upon the counter, and came running back to fetch them, and committed hundreds of the like mistakes in the best humor possible; while the Grocer and his people were so frank and fresh that the polished hearts with which they fastened their aprons behind might have been their own, worn outside for general inspection, and for Christmas daws to peck at if they chose.

But soon the steeples called good people all, to church and chapel, and away they came, flocking through the streets in their best clothes, and with their gayest faces. And at the same time there emerged from scores of bye streets, lanes, and nameless turnings, innumerable people, carrying their dinners to the bakers' shops. The sight of these poor revelers appeared to interest the Spirit very much, for he stood with Scrooge beside him in a bakers doorway, and taking off the covers as their bearers passed, sprinkled incense on their dinners from his torch. And it was a very uncommon kind of torch, for once or twice when there were angry words between some dinner-carriers who had jostled with each other, he shed a few drops of water on them from it, and their good humor was restored directly. For they said, it was a shame to quarrel upon Christmas Day. And so it was! God love it, so it was!

In time the bells ceased, and the bakers' were shut up; and yet there was a genial shadowing forth of all these dinners and the progress of their cooking, in the thawed blotch of wet above each baker's oven; where the pavement smoked as if its stones were cooking too.

"Is there a peculiar flavor in what you sprinkle from your torch?" asked Scrooge.

"There is. My own."

"Would it apply to any kind of dinner on this day?" asked Scrooge.

"To any kindly given. To a poor one most."

"Why to a poor one most?" asked Scrooge.

"Because it needs it most."

"Spirit," said Scrooge, after a moment's thought, "I wonder you, of all the beings in the many worlds about us, should desire to cramp these people's opportunities of innocent enjoyment."

"I!" cried the Spirit.

"You would deprive them of their means of dining every seventh day, often the only day on which they can be said to dine at all," said Scrooge. "Wouldn't you?"

"I!" cried the Spirit.

"You seek to close these places on the Seventh Day?" said Scrooge. "And it comes to the same thing."

«I seek!" exclaimed the Spirit.

"Forgive me if I am wrong. It has been done in your name, or at least in that of your family," said Scrooge.

"There are some upon this earth of yours," returned the Spirit, "who lay claim to know us, and who do their deeds of passion, pride, ill-will, hatred, envy, bigotry, and selfishness in our name; who are as strange to us and all our kith and kin, as if they had never lived. Remember that, and charge their doings on themselves, not us."

Scrooge promised that he would; and they went on, invisible, as they had been before, into the suburbs of the town. It was a remarkable quality of the Ghost (which Scrooge had observed at the baker's) that notwithstanding his gigantic size, he could accommodate himself to any place with ease; and that he stood beneath a low roof quite as gracefully and like a supernatural creature, as it was possible he could have done in any lofty hall.

And perhaps it was the pleasure the good Spirit had in showing off this power of his, or else it was his own kind, generous, hearty nature, and his sympathy with all poor men, that led him straight to Scrooge's clerk's; for there he went, and took Scrooge with him, holding to his robe; and on the threshold of the door the Spirit smiled, and stopped to bless Bob Cratchit's dwelling with the sprinklings of his torch. Think of that! Bob had but fifteen "Bob" a-week himself; he pocketed on Saturdays but fifteen copies of his Christian name; and yet the Ghost of Christmas Present blessed his four-roomed house!

Then up rose Mrs. Cratchit, Cratchit's wife, dressed out but poorly in a twice-turned gown, but brave in ribbons, which are cheap and make a goodly show for sixpence; and she laid the cloth, assisted by Belinda Cratchit, second of her daughters, also brave in ribbons; while Master Peter Cratchit plunged a fork into the saucepan of potatoes, and getting the corners of his monstrous shirt-collar (Bob's private property, conferred upon his son and heir in honor of the day) into his mouth, rejoiced to find himself so gallantly attired, and yearned to show his linen in the fashionable Parks. And now two smaller Cratchits, boy and girl, came tearing in, screaming that outside the baker's they had smelt the goose, and known it for their own; and basking in luxurious thoughts of sage-and-onion, these young Cratchits danced about the table, and exalted Master Peter Cratchit to the skies, while he (not proud, although his collars nearly choked him) blew the fire, until the slow potatoes bubbling up, knocked loudly at the saucepan-lid to be let out and peeled.

"What has ever got your precious father then," said Mrs. Cratchit. "And your brother, Tiny Tim! And Martha warn't as late last Christmas Day by half-an-hour!"

"Here's Martha, mother!" said a girl, appearing as she spoke.

"Here's Martha, mother!" cried the two young Cratchits. "Hurrah! There's such a goose, Martha!"

"Why, bless your heart alive, my dear, how late you are!" said Mrs. Cratchit, kissing her a dozen times, and taking off her shawl and bonnet for her, with officious zeal.

"We'd a deal of work to finish up last night," replied the girl, "and had to clear away this morning, mother!"

"Well! Never mind so long as you are come," said Mrs. Cratchit. "Sit ye down before the fire, my dear, and have a warm, Lord bless ye!"

"No no! There's father coming," cried the two young Cratchits, who were everywhere at once. "Hide Martha, hide!"

So Martha hid herself, and in came little Bob, the father, with at least three feet of comforter exclusive of the fringe, hanging down before him; and his thread-bare clothes darned up and brushed, to look seasonable; and Tiny Tim upon his shoulder. Alas for Tiny Tim, he bore a little crutch, and had his limbs supported by an iron frame!

"Why, where's our Martha?" cried Bob Cratchit looking round.

"Not coming," said Mrs. Cratchit.

"Not coming!" said Bob, with a sudden declension in his high spirits; for he had been Tim's blood horse all the way from church, and had come home rampant. "Not coming upon Christmas Day!"

Martha didn't like to see him disappointed, if it were only in joke; so she came out prematurely from behind the closet door, and ran into his arms, while the two young

Cratchits hustled Tiny Tim, and bore him off into the wash-house, that he might hear the pudding singing in the copper.

"And how did little Tim behave?" asked Mrs. Cratchit, when she had rallied Bob on his credulity and Bob had hugged his daughter to his heart's content.

"As good as gold," said Bob, "and better. Somehow he gets thoughtful sitting by himself so much, and thinks the strangest things you ever heard. He told me, coming home, that he hoped the people saw him in the church, because he was a cripple, and it might be pleasant to them to remember upon Christmas Day, who made lame beggars walk and blind men see."

Bob's voice was tremulous when he told them this, and trembled more when he said that Tiny Tim was growing strong and hearty.

His active little crutch was heard upon the floor, and back came Tiny Tim before another word was spoken, escorted by his brother and sister to his stool beside the fire; and while Bob, turning up his cuffs—as if, poor fellow, they were capable of being made more shabby—compounded some hot mixture in a jug with gin and lemons, and stirred it round and round and put it on the hob to simmer; Master Peter and the two ubiquitous young Cratchits went to fetch the goose, with which they soon returned in high procession.

Such a bustle ensued that you might have thought a goose the rarest of all birds; a feathered phenomenon, to which a black swan was a matter of course: and in truth it was something very like it in that house. Mrs. Cratchit made the gravy (ready beforehand in a little saucepan) hissing hot; Master Peter mashed the potatoes with incredible vigor; Miss Belinda sweetened up the apple-sauce; Martha dusted the hot plates; Bob took Tiny Tim beside him in a tiny corner at the table; the two young Cratchits set chairs for everybody, not forgetting themselves, and mounting guard upon their posts, crammed spoons into their mouths, lest they should shriek for goose before their turn came to be helped. At last the dishes were set on, and grace was said. It was succeeded by a breathless pause, as Mrs. Cratchit, looking slowly all along the carving-knife, prepared to plunge it in the breast; but when she did, and when the long expected gush of stuffing issued forth, one murmur of delight arose all round the board, and even Tiny Tim, excited by the two young Cratchits, beat on the table with the handle of his knife, and feebly cried Hurrah!

There never was such a goose. Bob said he didn't believe there ever was such a goose cooked. Its tenderness and flavor, size and cheapness, were the themes of universal admiration. Eked out by the apple-sauce and mashed potatoes, it was a sufficient dinner for the whole family; indeed, as Mrs. Cratchit said with great delight (surveying one small atom of a bone upon the dish), they hadn't ate it all at last! Yet every one had had enough, and the youngest Cratchits in particular, were steeped in sage and onion to the eyebrows! But now, the plates being changed by Miss

Belinda, Mrs. Cratchit left the room alone—too nervous to bear witnesses—to take the pudding up, and bring it in.

Suppose it should not be done enough! Suppose it should break in turning out! Suppose somebody should have got over the wall of the back-yard, and stolen it, while they were merry with the goose: a supposition at which the two young Cratchits became livid! All sorts of horrors were supposed.

Hallo! A great deal of steam! The pudding was out of the copper. A smell like a washing-day! That was the cloth. A smell like an eating-house, and a pastry cook's next door to each other, with a laundress's next door to that! That was the pudding. In half a minute Mrs. Cratchit entered: flushed, but smiling proudly: with the pudding, like a speckled cannon-ball, so hard and firm, blazing in half of half-a-quartern of ignited brandy, and bedight with Christmas holly stuck into the top.

Oh, a wonderful pudding! Bob Cratchit said, and calmly too, that he regarded it as the greatest success achieved by Mrs. Cratchit since their marriage. Mrs. Cratchit said that now the weight was off her mind, she would confess she had had her doubts about the quantity of flour. Everybody had something to say about it, but nobody said or thought it was at all a small pudding for a large family. It would have been flat heresy to do so. Any Cratchit would have blushed to hint at such a thing.

FOOD

There never was such a goose . . . it was a sufficient dinner for the whole family; indeed, as Mrs. Cratchit said with great delight (surveying one small atom of a bone upon the dish), they hadn't ate it all at last!

Upon meeting Mr. Charles Dickens himself, British actor J. L. Toole told the famous author a particularly poignant story about his time playing Bob Cratchit in a stage production of *A Christmas Carol.* Apparently, Dickens was quite touched by the anecdote.

Every night at eight, for forty nights, I had to carve a goose and a plum-pudding...a real goose and a real plum-pudding, which were served smoking hot for Mrs. Cratchit and the seven little Cratchits, of course including Tiny Tim. The children always had enormous portions given them, and all ate heartily every night; but what really troubled me was the conduct of the little girl who played Tiny Tim. That child's appetite appalled me. I could not help noticing the extraordinary rapidity with which she consumed what I gave her, and she looked so wan and thin and so pitiful, that her face used to positively haunt me.

I used to say to myself before I began, "Well, Tiny Tim shall have enough this time, at all events" and I piled her plate more and more each evening, until, I remember, she had on one occasion nearly half the bird, besides potatoes and apple-sauce. It puzzled me to know how she could even carry it away to the fireplace, where she sat on a low stool, in accordance with the story, much less eat it. To my amazement she carried it off and cleared her plate as quickly and as eagerly as ever, pushing forward for plum-pudding with the others. I grew alarmed, and spoke to Mrs. Alfred Mellon, who was playing Mrs. Cratchit, respecting this strange phenomenon.

"I don't like it," I said. "I can't conceive where a poor, delicate little thing like that puts the food. Besides, although I like the children to enjoy a treat" — and how they kept on enjoying it for forty nights was a mystery, for I got into such a condition that if I dined at friend's house and goose

was on the table, I regarded it as a personal affront— I said, referring to Tiny Tim, "I don't like greediness; and it is additionally repulsive in a refined-looking, delicate little thing like this. Besides it destroys the sentiment of the situation— and when I, Bob, ought to feel most pathetic, I am always wondering where the goose and the pudding are, or whether anything serious in the way of a fit will happen to Tiny Tim before the audience, in consequence of her unnatural gorging."

Mrs. Mellon laughed at me at first, but eventually we decided to watch Tiny Tim together. We watched as well as we could, and the moment Tiny Tim was seated and began to eat, we observed a curious shuffling movement at the stage fireplace, and everything that I had given her, goose and potatoes and apple-sauce, disappeared behind the sham stove, the child pretending to eat as hearty as ever from the empty plate.

When the performance was over, Mrs. Mellon and myself asked the little girl what became of the food she did not eat, and, after a little hesitation, frightened lest she should get into trouble, which we assured her could not happen, she confessed that her little sister (I should mention that they were the children of one of the scene-shifters.), waited on the other side of the stage fireplace for the supplies, and that the whole family enjoyed a hearty supper every night

*out of the plentiful portions to which I, as Bob, had as-
sisted Tiny Tim.*

*Dickens was very much interested in the incident. When I
had finished, he smiled a little sadly, I thought, and then
shaking me by the hand he said, "Ah, you ought to have
given her the whole goose."*

If this ghost story is about anything, it's about
food.

Ancient pagan tales, as well as contemporary
urban legends, have always maintained that ghosts
cannot eat. Remaining true to this traditional un-
derstanding Dickens never allows the ghosts in his
story to taste even so much as a crumb of food.
However, this does not keep him from flavoring his
ghost story with an overabundance of culinary de-
lights. He references food, drink, eating, banquet-
ing, cooking, kitchens, ovens, tables, ingredients,
recipes, pots, pans, forks, knives, spoons, soups,
and sauces over 200 times in a book that doesn't
even amount to as many pages.

The Ghost of Christmas Present introduces
himself by displaying before Scrooge no less than
seventeen different dishes! And of course, the
Cratchit's Christmas feast (which Dickens always
seemed to relish as his favorite part of the story) is
a word picture equal to Norman Rockwell's famous

painting "Freedom From Want" as a celebrated illustration of the joy a family might experience upon the presentation of a perfectly roasted fowl. These are the most well-known references to food and feasting in *A Christmas Carol*, but there are many more. Both Fezziwig's ball and Fred's dinner party are filled with food, but let us not forget the green grocers, spice merchants, fruit sellers, fish mongers, poulterers, eating houses, pastry cooks, and bake shops! Dickens even goes so far (excuse the pun) as to sandwich all these descriptions of food and drink between some very creative culinary references. In the early pages of the story he describes the "hungry cold" gnawing at one's nose like a dog with a bone and makes a biblical reference to a cannibalistic cobra gobbling up Scrooge's distracted thoughts. Near the end of the novel there is talk of the traditional lunch served after a funeral, and the close and crowded graveyard is described as being "choked up with too much burying; fat with repleted appetite."

Setting aside the nauseating visual image of one snake eating another and the idea of a "fat graveyard," I find that reading *A Christmas Carol* always leaves me starving! And no little snack of cheese and crackers will do. I'm going to want a feast of things cooked, roasted, boiled, baked, simmered, spiced, and served up properly on Christmas china laid out on a cloth-covered table decorated with candles and a centerpiece. And it goes without saying that the dessert should be presented flambé. Consequently, I considered writing a cookbook featuring all of my favorite Dickens delicacies, but several books of this variety have already been produced. And, as the saying goes, there is no sense in chewing spaghetti twice. So, I shall simply report that as a result of my love for this story I have produced from my personal test kitchen a ten-pound goose roasted to my family's satisfaction and several excellent Christmas puddings that would rival Mrs. Cratchit's finest achievement. I have also consumed a variety of festive holiday beverages including smoking bishop and a Victorian concoction called "A Yard of Flannel," which consists of heated beer and raw eggs garnished with cinnamon and nutmeg. (Common, everyday eggnog doesn't hold a candle!)

I often perform this story in restaurants. In my opinion, it is the very best way to consume the tale, because in that particular setting all five senses are fully employed. Patrons will of course hear the wonderful words of Dickens and relish them like sugar plums. However, the hearing of the story is greatly enhanced for the listeners by being seated at tables instead of forward facing rows as you would find in a typical theatre or auditorium.

Seeing one another, instead of all looking toward the stage, restaurant patrons can observe the effect of Dickens' words on the faces of their friends and loved ones. This arrangement inevitably leads to a much more intimate sharing of the experience. Friends poke and nudge one another upon hearing a particularly witty bit of Dickens' drollery. When Mr. and Mrs. Fezziwig dance or Topper steals a glance at the plump sister, lovers reach beneath the table to hold hands. When Bob Cratchit draws Tiny Tim closer to his side, parents instinctively slip their arms around their children.

Moreover, the backstage of this particular performance space is not a dressing room but a kitchen, and the most delicious aromas come wafting out of the wings just about the time I speak the words of Ebenezer Scrooge when he says to the Ghost of Jacob Marley "You may be an undigested bit of beef, a blot of mustard, a crumb of cheese, a fragment of an underdone potato. There's more of gravy than of grave about you, whatever you are!" And shortly following this little litany of menu items, the salad course is served, followed in rapid succession by the soup and the Ghost of Christmas Past. Then the entree with several sides arrives with the Ghost of Christmas Present. Finally the Ghost of Christmas Future is brought on not so much with the effects of a theater's fog machine as with clouds of whip cream, spun sugar, and chiffon. I particularly enjoy telling the story at 211 Main Cafe & Bakery, in Lavonia, Georgia, where the spirit most resembling the Grim Reaper is accompanied by huge slices of six-layer cake with cream cheese frosting! One might conclude if you should "feed a cold and starve a fever," you get rid of a ghost by gluttony! It is the same in whatever restaurant I perform. If the chef is the least bit familiar with the story, the menu will be an illustration of the saying, "too much is not enough!"

And why not? For Christmas is the season of excess. Not only do we eat too much, we spend too much, decorate too much (You should see all the blowups in my neighbor's yard!), stay up too late watching way too many Christmas movies, linger at a friend's party too long, and annually load the Christmas tree with an ever-increasing number of ornaments. And this is as it should be—an excessive celebration of excessive love. Simply note the words of familiar carols and you'll see what I say is true. We sing with joy to the world of angels from the realms of glory proclaiming peace o'er all the earth from God on high forevermore coming down from heaven to be born as a baby in a lowly manger. "God Rest you merry, gentlemen! Let nothing you dismay. Remember Christ our Savior was born on Christmas Day. To save us all from Satan's power when we were gone astray." You cannot celebrate those "tidings of comfort and joy" in a small way. So praise the Lord and pass the mashed potatoes!

At last the dinner was all done, the cloth was cleared, the hearth swept, and the fire made up. The compound in the jug being tasted and considered perfect, apples and oranges were put upon the table, and a shovel-full of chestnuts on the fire. Then all the Cratchit family drew round the hearth, in what Bob Cratchit called a circle, meaning half a one; and at Bob Cratchit's elbow stood the family display of glass; two tumblers, and a custard-cup without a handle.

These held the hot stuff from the jug, however, as well as golden goblets would have done; and Bob served it out with beaming looks, while the chestnuts on the fire sputtered and crackled noisily. Then Bob proposed:

"A Merry Christmas to us all, my dears. God bless us!"

Which all the family re-echoed.

"God bless us every one!" said Tiny Tim, the last of all.

He sat very close to his father's side, upon his little stool. Bob held his withered little hand in his, as if he loved the child, and wished to keep him by his side, and dreaded that he might be taken from him.

"Spirit," said Scrooge, with an interest he had never felt before, "tell me if Tiny Tim will live."

"I see a vacant seat," replied the Ghost, "in the poor chimney corner, and a crutch without an owner, carefully preserved. If these shadows remain unaltered by the Future, the child will die."

"No, no," said Scrooge. "Oh no, kind Spirit! say he will be spared."

"If these shadows remain unaltered by the Future, none other of my race," returned the Ghost, "will find him here. What then? If he be like to die, he had better do it, and decrease the surplus population."

Scrooge hung his head to hear his own words quoted by the Spirit, and was overcome with penitence and grief.

"Man," said the Ghost, "if man you be in heart, not adamant, forbear that wicked cant until you have discovered What the surplus is, and Where it is. Will you decide what men shall live, what men shall die? It may be, that in the sight of Heaven, you are more worthless and less fit to live than millions like this poor man's child. Oh God! to hear the Insect on the leaf pronouncing on the too much life among his hungry brothers in the dust!"

Scrooge bent before the Ghost's rebuke, and trembling cast his eyes upon the ground. But he raised them speedily, on hearing his own name.

"Mr. Scrooge!" said Bob; "I'll give you Mr. Scrooge, the Founder of the Feast!"

"The Founder of the Feast indeed!" cried Mrs. Cratchit, reddening. "I wish I had him here. I'd give him a piece of my mind to feast upon, and I hope he'd have a good appetite for it."

"My dear," said Bob, "the children; Christmas Day."

"It should be Christmas Day, I am sure," said she, "on which one drinks the health of such an odious, stingy, hard, unfeeling man as Mr. Scrooge. You know he is, Robert! Nobody knows it better than you do, poor fellow!"

"My dear," was Bob's mild answer, "Christmas Day."

"I'll drink his health for your sake and the Day's," said Mrs. Cratchit, "not for his. Long life to him! A merry Christmas and a happy new year!—he'll be very merry and very happy, I have no doubt!"

The children drank the toast after her. It was the first of their proceedings which had no heartiness in it. Tiny Tim drank it last of all, but he didn't care twopence for it. Scrooge was the Ogre of the family. The mention of his name cast a dark shadow on the party, which was not dispelled for full five minutes.

After it had passed away, they were ten times merrier than before, from the mere relief of Scrooge the Baleful being done with. Bob Cratchit told them how he had a situation in his eye for Master Peter, which would bring in, if obtained, full five-and-sixpence weekly. The two young Cratchits laughed tremendously at the idea of Peter's being a man of business; and Peter himself looked thoughtfully at the fire from between his collars, as if he were deliberating what particular investments he should favor when he came into the receipt of that bewildering income. Martha, who was a poor apprentice at a milliner's, then told them what kind of work she had to do, and how many hours she worked at a stretch, and how she meant to lie a-bed to-morrow morning for a good long rest; to-morrow being a holiday she passed at home. Also how she had seen a countess and a lord some days before, and how the lord "was much about as tall as Peter;" at which Peter pulled up his collars so high that you couldn't have seen his head if you had been there. All this time the chestnuts and the jug went round and round; and bye and bye they had a song, about a lost child traveling in the snow, from Tiny Tim; who had a plaintive little voice, and sang it very well indeed.

There was nothing of high mark in this. They were not a handsome family; they were not well dressed; their shoes were far from being water-proof; their clothes were scanty; and Peter might have known, and very likely did, the inside of a pawnbroker's. But they were happy, grateful, pleased with one another, and contented with the time; and when they faded, and looked happier yet in the bright sprinklings of the Spirit's torch at parting, Scrooge had his eye upon them, and especially on Tiny Tim, until the last.

CLOTHING

There was nothing of high mark in all of this. They were not a handsome family; they were not well dressed; their shoes were far from being water-proof; their clothes were scanty...

Several years ago I had a performance of "The Carol" in Greenville, South Carolina that concluded late on a Saturday night. The very next day I was scheduled for an afternoon matinee four hours away. My plan was to get up early, drive to my next destination, take a power nap in the car, jump into my costume, perform the show, then go home and fall into bed to catch up on much needed rest. Consequently, I did not plan to attend church services that particular Sunday morning. I was on the road by eight with a tall, steaming cup of coffee in the cup holder and a sack of powdered donuts on the passenger seat next to me.

My large top hat, the signature piece of any gentleman's Dickensian costume, was carefully placed on the back seat of the car, far away from the powdered donuts. It wouldn't do to get powdered sugar all over that hat. It is magnificent. Tall (six and one-half inches), brimmed (steamed to just the right curvature), trimmed (wide grosgrain ribbon), and dark pecan in color (more festive than the formal black). When I set it atop my head, it raises my overall height to six feet, eight-and-one-half inches. The top hat is definitely the crowning accessory to my costume ensemble of black leather boots, dark brown woolen striped trousers, a fine linen shirt, a green and gold silk jacquard waistcoat, moss-colored regal cravat, and a gray woolen frock coat trimmed with dark brown velvet lapels. Not to mention my gold watch and chain with jingly gewgaws—decorative charms serving no particular purpose. A well-dressed gentleman of Victorian England would sport one charm; an overdressed gentleman might risk two shiny luck charms hanging from his watch chain. I display five. In keeping with Victorian fashion, I am very proud of my costume. The frock coat is custom tailored and hand-sewn from twenty-one individual pieces of fabric!

According to Daniel Pool's description of daily life in nineteenth century England, a well-dressed gentleman chose every article of clothing with the utmost care. He depended upon his fashion sense to communicate his social standing to strangers he passed in the street. The trend ran toward ostentation. So much so that even shirts and underwear, hidden by layers of more luxurious outer garments, were carefully considered. Linen had "snob appeal because it dirtied so quickly that if you could wear clean linen all the time you obviously had enough money to be a gentleman." This fact is what Dickens is referring to when he describes Master Peter Cratchit's personal pride in wearing his father's good shirt collar on Christmas Day and feeling so gallantly attired he yearns to show his linen in the fashionable parks.

Other than this specific detail about shirt linen, Dickens doesn't give much time or space for descriptions of his characters' clothing. There are brief references to hats, ribbons, scarves, dress trims, and an offhanded mention of the Welch wig on top of Fezziwig's presumably bald pate. (By the way, a Welch wig is a knitted cap, not a formal white powdered wig like you often see in stage and film adaptations. They always get that wrong.) But Dickens doesn't ever really describe a character's costume from head to toe. At least not the mortals. The ghosts, on the other hand, are described like fashion models displaying haute couture on a Parisian runway. Every detail of each phantom's attire is so carefully laid out we must conclude each robe or hat or accessory is laden with significant symbolic meaning. The Ghost of Christmas Past displays a glowing, luminescent belt reflecting the fickleness of mortal memory. The Ghost of Christmas Present wears a rusted scabbard without a sword, which is a clear reference to peace on Earth. And of course, the Ghost of Christmas Future is draped in deep black to make us think of the Grim Reaper. One might conclude, contrary to the popular saying, clothes do not make the man, but they are indispensable to a ghost! I think that's exactly what Dickens is saying in a creative way. He is reminding his Victorian reader the outward appearance means little or nothing. It's the Spirit that counts! I came to that conclusion while driving through Greenville, South Carolina on a Sunday morning sipping coffee and munching powdered donuts.

I was just about twenty minutes into my four-hour drive when I pulled up to a red light at the corner of Stone Avenue and Rutherford Street. This is the address of Triune Mercy Center. Triune is a church dedicated to empowering Greenville's disadvantaged community by offering relief in the form of meals, medical and legal aid, addiction and mental health counseling, and other social services through a network of staff, volunteers, congregants, and community partners. I was familiar with this church because I used to live in Greenville and still have a good friend who volunteers there with a storytelling/theater therapy program. When I stopped at the red light, I noticed several people—I shouldn't assume, but presumably homeless—walking into the church. I remember feeling a little pang of guilt because they were heading to early morning prayer and I was racing off to do a show (not exactly the most pious way to occupy the early hours of the first day of the week).

Seemingly out of nowhere, there appeared before me a man in the crosswalk. Taking advantage of the long red light, he ambled across the street in front of my car without a bit of rush or hurry. He was dressed in the typical fashion of someone living on the streets—several layers of worn out, dirty clothing covered by a ragged coat that didn't keep him warm so much as it provided an extra layer of padding when he slept on the sidewalk. However, the most curious thing about this man was on the crown of his head sat a tall (six-and-one-half inches), brimmed (steamed to just the right curvature), trimmed (wide grosgrain ribbon), dark pecan-colored (more festive than the formal black) top hat! I instinctively looked over my shoulder to see if my $250 topper had somehow been nicked from the back seat of my locked car. Nope, my hat was secure, but this fellow was wearing one, in pristine condition, just like mine! Well, Merry Christmas! I had to go into the church and see this thing which had come to pass.

When the light changed, I made a left turn instead of continuing straight through the intersection and drove behind the church to the parking lot. I hurriedly parked the car and rushed around the building to the front entrance. Hearing organ music from inside as I approached the door and realizing I was not on a ghost hunt but rather about to enter a sacred space, I slowed down and stopped to say good morning to the greeter at the door and take a worship bulletin from his hand. As I entered the sanctuary, there were already a good number of people sitting in the pews. I stood in the back and scanned the heads for a top hat. Of course, the hat had been removed out of respect for all things holy, and I could not see it anywhere. It wouldn't do to go up and down the center aisle peering into every pew, so I slid into a seat and waited. The organ played quietly, a few people spoke in hushed tones, but mostly they just sat and listened or bowed their heads in prayer. By this point it was about eight twenty-five. I didn't see a starting time printed on my worship bulletin, so I turned to speak to the lady seated directly behind me.

"Excuse me," I whispered. "What time does the service start?"

She informed me the service did not begin for another hour, but folks came in early to pray, enjoy some fellowship, and frankly, to get warm. I nodded and turned back around. Considering the start of the service was still an hour away, and who knew how long it would take me to find my man after the amen, I decided to take my leave.

I stood up and stepped out into the aisle. As I turned to go, the lady I had spoken to smiled and said, "I wish you could stay."

I sat back down struggling against the urge to ask her, "Did you see a man in a tall, brimmed, trimmed, dark pecan-colored top hat walk in here?" Instead I asked, "Do you know most of the people here?"

"Not really," she replied. "I attend another church across town, but I volunteer at the food pantry here during the week. I often come for this early Sunday service before going to my own church later in the day."

"You come to this church before going to your own church?" I asked.

"Often," she assured me.

"May I ask why?"

The lady turned to me and said, "Because here it doesn't matter who you are or where you come from. It doesn't matter what's in your past or what you struggle with. Nobody cares about what kind of car you drive, or if you have a car at all. *Nobody cares how you are dressed.* None of that matters. Here it is all about Spirit!"

She had no idea I had come into the sanctuary chasing a status symbol, but her words were the equivalent of a Sunday morning mic drop. Boom.

As I stood back up to go, I reached into my pocket for my wallet. I handed her a twenty dollar bill and asked her to put it into the collection basket on my behalf.

"What's this?"

"An offering," I said. And then to myself, "a hat tip, you might say."

By this time it was getting dark, and snowing pretty heavily; and as Scrooge and the Spirit went along the streets, the brightness of the roaring fires in kitchens, parlors, and all sorts of rooms, was wonderful. Here, the flickering of the blaze showed preparations for a cosy dinner, with hot plates baking through and through before the fire, and deep red curtains, ready to be drawn,

to shut out cold and darkness. There, all the children of
the house were running out into the snow to meet their
married sisters, brothers, cousins, uncles, aunts, and be
the first to greet them. Here, again, were shadows on the
window-blind of guests assembling; and there a group of
handsome girls, all hooded and fur-booted, and all chattering at once, tripped lightly off to some near neighbor's
house; where, wo upon the single man who saw them enter—artful witches: well they knew it—in a glow!

But if you had judged from the numbers of people on
their way to friendly gatherings, you might have thought
that no one was at home to give them welcome when they
got there, instead of every house expecting company, and
piling up its fires half-chimney high. Blessings on it, how
the Ghost exulted! How it bared its breadth of breast, and
opened its capacious palm, and floated on, outpouring,
with a generous hand, its bright and harmless mirth on
everything within its reach! The very lamplighter, who ran
on before dotting the dusky street with specks of light, and
who was dressed to spend the evening somewhere, laughed
out loudly as the Spirit passed: though little kenned the
lamplighter that he had any company but Christmas!

And now, without a word of warning from the Ghost,
they stood upon a bleak and desert moor, where monstrous masses of rude stone were cast about, as though
it were the burial-place of giants; and water spread itself
wheresoever it listed—or would have done so, but for the
frost that held it prisoner; and nothing grew but moss and

furze, and coarse, rank grass. Down in the west the setting sun had left a streak of fiery red, which glared upon the desolation for an instant, like a sullen eye, and frowning lower, lower, lower yet, was lost in the thick gloom of darkest night.

"What place is this?" asked Scrooge.

"A place where Miners live, who labour in the bowels of the earth," returned the Spirit. "But they know me. See!"

A light shone from the window of a hut, and swiftly they advanced towards it. Passing through the wall of mud and stone, they found a cheerful company assembled round a glowing fire. An old, old man and woman, with their children and their children's children, and another generation beyond that, all decked out gaily in their holiday attire. The old man, in a voice that seldom rose above the howling of the wind upon the barren waste, was singing them a Christmas song; it had been a very old song when he was a boy; and from time to time they all joined in the chorus. So surely as they raised their voices, the old man got quite blithe and loud; and so surely as they stopped, his vigor sank again.

The Spirit did not tarry here, but bade Scrooge hold his robe, and passing on above the moor, sped whither? Not to sea? To sea. To Scrooge's horror, looking back, he saw the last of the land, a frightful range of rocks, behind them; and his ears were deafened by the thundering of water, as it rolled, and roared, and raged among the dreadful caverns it had worn, and fiercely tried to undermine the earth.

Built upon a dismal reef of sunken rocks, some league or so from shore, on which the waters chafed and dashed, the wild year through, there stood a solitary lighthouse. Great heaps of sea-weed clung to its base, and storm-birds—born of the wind one might suppose, as sea-weed of the water—rose and fell about it, like the waves they skimmed.

But even here, two men who watched the light had made a fire, that through the loophole in the thick stone wall shed out a ray of brightness on the awful sea. Joining their horny hands over the rough table at which they sat, they wished each other Merry Christmas in their can of grog; and one of them: the elder, too, with his face all damaged and scarred with hard weather, as the figure-head of an old ship might be: struck up a sturdy song that was like a Gale in itself.

Again the Ghost sped on, above the black and heaving sea—on, on—until, being far away, as he told Scrooge, from any shore, they lighted on a ship. They stood beside the helmsman at the wheel, the look-out in the bow, the officers who had the watch; dark, ghostly figures in their several stations; but every man among them hummed a Christmas tune, or had a Christmas thought, or spoke below his breath to his companion of some bygone Christmas Day, with homeward hopes belonging to it. And every man on board, waking or sleeping, good or bad, had had a kinder word for another on that day than on any day in the year; and had shared to some extent in its festivities; and had remembered those he cared for at a distance, and had known that they delighted to remember him.

SONG

The old man...was singing them a Christmas song; it had been a very old song when he was a boy; and from time to time they all joined in the chorus.

Many people find it ironic that Dickens titled his story *A Christmas Carol* when he only references one popular holiday song in the entire work: "God Rest Ye Merry Gentlemen." However, in my mind the tale stands alongside two great musical works—Tchaikovsky's Nutcracker and Handel's Messiah—as perfect expressions of the season. Handel wrote a sacred work quickly adopted by the church and Tchaikovsky composed a ballet for the theatre; Dickens pens a simple song to be sung in the home. G. K. Chesterton puts it this way. "The story sings from end to end like a happy man going home; and, like a happy and good man, when it cannot sing it yells. It is lyric and exclamatory, from the first exclamatory words of it. It is strictly a Christmas Carol."

These days any song that includes snow, sleigh bells, or Santa Claus is called a Christmas carol, but actually a carol is a particular type of Christmas song. Rosie Pentreath of Classic FM Digital Radio identifies the essential elements: "Stirring melodies are usually sprinkled with minor and diminished chords—think of the mix of major and minor melody lines in 'God Rest Ye Merry Gentlemen'—in popular Christmas carols and songs. This all underpins lyrics that are nostalgic, and often as sombre as they are uplifting and inspiring. Centered around the miraculous story of Jesus's [sic] birth, of course, the overall message of the Christmas carol is one of awe, humility, hope, and abundant joy." Is that not an accurate description of Dickens' tale? Especially the mix of nostalgia, somberness, and abundant joy? However, it would be quite a lot to print on the title page, so the author went with the understated "A Christmas Carol, in Prose, being a Ghost Story of Christmas."

Dickens may have described his holiday offering as a ghost story, but it is structured like a Christmas hymn. Each chapter is marked as a stave, and the basic plot parallels the story told in "God Rest Ye Merry, Gentlemen." In the traditional carol, we learn all humanity was trapped in "Satan's power." This is the very description of Scrooge in my way of thinking. Shepherds are frightened by an angel, but are quickly assured the heavenly visitor brings good news of their salvation. Scrooge is more than a little startled by some otherworldly visitors, but grows to understand their purpose is for his good. The shepherds brave life-threatening "tempest, storm, and wind" in their rush to Bethlehem to confirm the words of the angel. Scrooge receives his confirmation in a graveyard. The carol concludes with an admonition to praise God and celebrate the brotherhood of man. Accompanied by the clamor of church bells, Scrooge immediately begins to joyfully practice charity in thought, word, and deed. Whether or not the parallelism was intentional on Dickens' part I cannot say, but it is nonetheless noteworthy.

The song "God Rest Ye Merry, Gentlemen" was an old one even in the nineteenth century, but still quite popular. In fact, it was well enough known that Dickens misquotes the words. There is no more certain evidence a song has become a popular street tune than people commonly misquoting the lyrics. Dickens writes "God *bless* you" rather than "God *rest* you." However, I wonder if the altered lyric wasn't rather purposeful. Perhaps, Dickens sought to clarify the meaning of the song. The word "rest" in this particular instance means "to keep, to cause to continue, to remain." It carries the connotation of preservation. "God rest ye merry, gentlemen" is shorthand for "Good sirs, may God preserve you in happiness and joy until the very end." The same idea is expressed at funerals when we pray that someone may "rest in peace." This would be too laborious to explain, but it fits neatly within the context of Scrooge contemplating his own mortality. Consequently, Dickens just makes a slight alteration from the original. Rather than lecture us on the meaning, as I have done in this essay, Dickens will prove the superior storyteller and show us this meaning in the graveyard scene.

Dickens also reinforces this idea of preservation in another way. He consistently uses the singing of Christmas carols to seal up in our hearts the true treasures of the Christmas season. Tiny Tim's plaintive little voice singing about a lost child traveling in the snow speaks to the poignant beauty of the meek and lowly. In the very old song shared by a coal miner with his children, grandchildren, and great-grandchildren, tradition is preserved for generations to come. The lighthouse keeper offers hope not only by tending the lamp that shines out a "ray of brightness on the awful sea," but also by striking up a "sturdy song that was like a gale in itself." Sailors express heartfelt affection for their home folks with a hummed Christmas tune. And finally, charity, which is the conscious choice to respond to scorn with forgiving laughter, is confirmed by harp and song at the conclusion of Fred's dinner party.

The placement of the single song quoted by Dickens is also noteworthy. He again is underscoring this idea of preservation. The joyful lyric "God bless ye merry, gentlemen" is cut short when Scrooge threatens physical violence toward a young caroler at his office door. After this, all the other songs in the novel are heard by Scrooge only when he is with the Ghost of Christmas Present. Why? Could it be Dickens wants us to realize that so many of the very sweetest moments of our lives are also so very short? These moments, not unlike the Christmas holiday itself, have a tremendous build-up, only to be gone in an instant. There is only one time in your life when you will sing your daughter her first lullaby. There is only one time when you will hear her lisp the "ABC Song" at her kindergarten graduation. The favorite song at her sweet sixteen birthday party will quickly fade into her college alma mater which will eventually be replaced by newlyweds having a first dance to "their" song.

We will never be able to re-live these moments, but we can sing the songs. This is why the dark alley, the death room, and the graveyard scenes with the Ghost of Christmas Future are so horrific—they are completely devoid of song.

Very often, when I book a performance of *A Christmas Carol*, the producer insists on hiring professional singers to provide pre-show music. In general, I am opposed to adding songs to my shows. I practice storytelling, not musical theater, and I firmly believe a well-told story does not need to be propped up by a song-and-dance routine. The story should stand on its own. However, this story is different. It is a ghost story. It begins with an unblinking look at death, haunts us with images of poverty and depravity, and threatens to leave us in a grave of our own digging. It is a hard story. But Dickens knew when you are telling a hard story, and maybe because you are telling a hard story, it must also sing. So he writes a ghost story that is really *A Christmas Carol*. Consequently, it is not uncommon for my audience to respond to the performance, not with applause but by bursting into songs of comfort and joy. And for that genuine and spontaneous response I can only say "God Bless Them, Every One!"

It was a great surprise to Scrooge, while listening to the moaning of the wind, and thinking what a solemn thing it was to move on through the lonely darkness over an unknown abyss, whose depths were secrets as profound as Death: it was a great surprise to Scrooge, while thus engaged, to hear a hearty laugh. It was a much greater surprise to Scrooge to recognize it as his own nephew's, and to find himself in a bright, dry, gleaming room, with the Spirit standing smiling by his side, and looking at that same nephew with approving affability!

"Ha, ha!" laughed Scrooge's nephew. "Ha, ha, ha!"

If you should happen, by any unlikely chance, to know a man more blest in a laugh than Scrooge's nephew, all I can say is, I should like to know him too. Introduce him to me, and I'll cultivate his acquaintance.

It is a fair, even-handed, noble adjustment of things, that while there is infection in disease and sorrow there is nothing in the world so irresistibly contagious as laughter and good-humor. When Scrooge's nephew laughed in this way: holding his sides, rolling his head, and twisting his face into the most extravagant contortions: Scrooge's niece, by marriage, laughed as heartily as he. And their assembled friends being not a bit behindhand, roared out, lustily.

"Ha, ha! Ha, ha, ha, ha!"

"He said that Christmas was a humbug, as I live!" cried Scrooge's nephew, "He believed it too!"

"More shame for him, Fred!" said Scrooge's niece, indignantly. Bless those women; they never do anything by halves. They are always in earnest.

She was very pretty: exceedingly pretty. With a dimpled, surprised-looking, capital face; a ripe little mouth, that seemed made to be kissed—as no doubt it was; all kinds of good little dots about her chin, that melted into one another when she laughed; and the sunniest pair of eyes you ever saw in any little creature's head. Altogether she was what you would have called provoking, you know; but satisfactory, too. Oh, perfectly satisfactory!

"He's a comical old fellow," said Scrooge's nephew, "that's the truth; and not so pleasant as he might be. However, his offenses carry their own punishment, and I have nothing to say against him."

"I'm sure he is very rich, Fred," hinted Scrooge's niece. "At least you always tell me so."

"What of that, my dear!" said Scrooge's nephew. "His wealth is of no use to him. He don't do any good with it. He don't make himself comfortable with it. He hasn't the satisfaction of thinking—ha, ha, ha!—that he is ever going to benefit Us with it."

"I have no patience with him," observed Scrooge's niece. Scrooge's niece's sisters, and all the other ladies, expressed the same opinion.

"Oh, I have!" said Scrooge's nephew. "I am sorry for him; I couldn't be angry with him if I tried. Who suffers by his ill whims? Himself, always. Here, he takes it into his head to dislike us, and he won't come and dine with us. What's the consequence? He don't lose much of a dinner."

"Indeed, I think he loses a very good dinner," interrupted Scrooge's niece. Everybody else said the same, and they must be allowed to have been competent judges, because they had just had dinner; and, with the dessert upon the table, were clustered round the fire, by lamplight.

"Well! I am very glad to hear it," said Scrooge's nephew, "because I haven't any great faith in these young housekeepers. What do you say, Topper?"

Topper had clearly got his eye upon one of Scrooge's niece's sisters, for he answered that a bachelor was a wretched outcast, who had no right to express an opinion on the subject. Whereat Scrooge's niece's sister—the plump one with the lace tucker: not the one with the roses—blushed.

"Do go on, Fred," said Scrooge's niece, clapping her hands. "He never finishes what he begins to say! He is such a ridiculous fellow!"

Scrooge's nephew reveled in another laugh, and as it was impossible to keep the infection off; though the plump sister tried hard to do it with aromatic vinegar; his example was unanimously followed.

"I was only going to say," said Scrooge's nephew, "that the consequence of his taking a dislike to us, and not making merry with us, is, as I think, that he loses some pleasant moments, which could do him no harm. I am sure he loses pleasanter companions than he can find in his own thoughts, either in his mouldy old office, or his dusty chambers. I mean to give him the same chance every year, whether he likes it or not, for I pity him. He may rail at Christmas till he dies, but he can't help thinking better of it—I defy him—if he finds me going there, in good temper, year after year, and saying Uncle Scrooge, how are you? If it only puts him in the vein to leave his poor clerk fifty pounds, that's something; and I think I shook him, yesterday."

It was their turn to laugh now, at the notion of his shaking Scrooge. But being thoroughly good-natured, and not much caring what they laughed at, so that they laughed at any rate, he encouraged them in their merriment, and passed the bottle, joyously.

After tea, they had some music. For they were a musical family, and knew what they were about, when they sung a Glee or Catch, I can assure you: especially Topper, who could growl away in the bass like a good one, and never swell the large veins in his forehead, or get red in the face over it. Scrooge's niece played well upon the harp; and played among other tunes a simple little air (a mere nothing: you might learn to whistle it in two minutes), which had been familiar to the child who fetched Scrooge from the boarding-school, as he had been reminded by the Ghost of Christmas Past. When this strain of music sounded, all the things that Ghost had shown him, came upon his mind; he softened more and more; and thought that if he could have listened to it often, years ago, he might have cultivated the kindnesses of life for his own happiness with

his own hands, without resorting to the sexton's spade that
buried Jacob Marley.

But they didn't devote the whole evening to music.
After a while they played at forfeits; for it is good to be
children sometimes, and never better than at Christmas,
when its mighty Founder was a child himself. Stop! There
was first a game at blindman's buff. Of course there was.
And I no more believe Topper was really blind than I believe he had eyes in his boots. My opinion is, that it was a
done thing between him and Scrooge's nephew; and that
the Ghost of Christmas Present knew it. The way he went
after that plump sister in the lace tucker, was an outrage
on the credulity of human nature. Knocking down the
fire-irons, tumbling over the chairs, bumping up against
the piano, smothering himself among the curtains, wherever she went, there went he. He always knew where the
plump sister was. He wouldn't catch anybody else. If you
had fallen up against him, as some of them did, and stood
there; he would have made a feint of endeavoring to seize
you, which would have been an affront to your under-
standing; and would instantly have sidled off in the direction of the plump sister. She often cried out that it wasn't
fair; and it really was not. But when at last, he caught her;
when, in spite of all her silken rustlings, and her rapid
flutterings past him, he got her into a corner whence there
was no escape; then his conduct was the most execrable.
For his pretending not to know her; his pretending that
it was necessary to touch her head-dress, and further to

assure himself of her identity by pressing a certain ring upon her finger, and a certain chain about her neck; was vile, monstrous! No doubt she told him her opinion of it, when, another blind-man being in office, they were so very confidential together, behind the curtains.

Scrooge's niece was not one of the blind-man's buff party, but was made comfortable with a large chair and a footstool, in a snug corner, where the Ghost and Scrooge were close behind her. But she joined in the forfeits, and loved her love to admiration with all the letters of the alphabet. Likewise at the game of How, When, and Where, she was very great, and to the secret joy of Scrooge's nephew, beat her sisters hollow: though they were sharp girls too, as Topper could have told you. There might have been twenty people there, young and old, but they all played, and so did Scrooge; for, wholly forgetting in the interest he had in what was going on, that his voice made no sound in their ears, he sometimes came out with his guess quite loud, and very often guessed right, too; for the sharpest needle, best Whitechapel, warranted not to cut in the eye, was not sharper than Scrooge: blunt as he took it in his head to be.

The Ghost was greatly pleased to find him in this mood, and looked upon him with such favor that he begged like a boy to be allowed to stay until the guests departed. But this the Spirit said could not be done.

"Here's a new game," said Scrooge. "One half hour, Spirit, only one!"

It was a Game called Yes and No, where Scrooge's nephew had to think of something, and the rest must find out what; he only answering to their questions yes or no as the case was. The brisk fire of questioning to which he was exposed, elicited from him that he was thinking of an animal, a live animal, rather a disagreeable animal, a savage animal, an animal that growled and grunted sometimes, and talked sometimes, and lived in London, and walked about the streets, and wasn't made a show of, and wasn't led by anybody, and didn't live in a menagerie, and was never killed in a market, and was not a horse, or an ass, or a cow, or a bull, or a tiger, or a dog, or a pig, or a cat, or a bear. At every fresh question that was put to him, this nephew burst into a fresh roar of laughter; and was so inexpressibly tickled, that he was obliged to get up off the sofa and stamp. At last the plump sister, falling into a similar state, cried out:

"I have found it out! I know what it is, Fred! I know what it is!"

"What is it?" cried Fred.

"It's your Uncle Scro-o-o-o-oge!"

Which it certainly was. Admiration was the universal sentiment, though some objected that the reply to "Is it a bear?" ought to have been "Yes;" inasmuch as an answer in the negative was sufficient to have diverted their thoughts from Mr. Scrooge, supposing they had ever had any tendency that way.

"He has given us plenty of merriment, I am sure," said Fred, "and it would be ungrateful not to drink his health. Here is a glass of mulled wine ready to our hand at the moment; and I say 'Uncle Scrooge!'"

"Well! Uncle Scrooge!" they cried.

"A Merry Christmas and a happy New Year to the old man, whatever he is!" said Scrooge's nephew. "He wouldn't take it from me, but may he have it, nevertheless. Uncle Scrooge!"

Uncle Scrooge had imperceptibly become so gay and light of heart, that he would have pledged the unconscious company in return, and thanked them in an inaudible speech, if the Ghost had given him time. But the whole scene passed off in the breath of the last word spoken by his nephew; and he and the Spirit were again upon their travels.

LAUGHTER

It is a fair, even-handed, noble adjustment of things, that while there is infection in disease and sorrow there is nothing in the world so irresistibly contagious as laughter and good-humor.

I never read this quotation without immediately recalling the tea party on the ceiling in the movie adaptation of *Mary Poppins*. Stop reading for a moment and look it up on YouTube. Go ahead. It's the best way to set the tone for the rest of this essay.

Laughter is ridiculously catching, and I very much treasure the type of friends who spread the infection on a regular basis. I hope you have those types of friends, too. You know, the ones you dare not sit next to during church because it will only lead to a disturbance.

I love private jokes. After more than twenty-five years of marriage my wife and I have a list of things we know will set the other person off. For instance, the poignant Irish folk song "O Danny Boy" never fails to crack us up. That's another YouTube thing. Search for the song and add the keyword "Muppets." Go ahead. I'll wait.

I hope by now you are laughing too. If not, I'll pray for you. Don't shrug. I'm serious.

When I was an expectant father with a referral from the adoption agency, I worried about the child's sense of humor. What if she was grave and sober? What would I do? Speaking of Mary Poppins, I very much desired a daughter like the character of little Jane Banks, who would be "rather inclined to giggle." I needn't have been concerned; my fear was quickly laid to rest. It happened at Christmastime.

My daughter came to us as a day-old infant in the early fall. As you might expect, my wife and I immediately began telling her stories and singing her songs. As her first Christmas approached, she was only three months old. Every night before we put her to bed, my wife Bonnie would sit in a rocking chair with Libby on her lap and I would tell a short story before Bonnie sang her to sleep. (This has always been the division of labor at bedtime in our house. I tell stories. Bonnie sings songs. The other way around would definitely be a comedy, let me assure you.) Since it was Advent, I decided to tell the whole Christmas story one bit at a time, beginning with the Annunciation and slowly working up to Jesus' birth.

On this particular evening, it was time to tell about Mary's visit to her cousin Elizabeth, who was sixth months pregnant after her own miraculous conception of John the Baptist. As the story goes, when Elizabeth heard Mary's greeting at the door, the baby in her belly jumped for joy. It's such a sweet and joyful passage. You should stop and read it. That's not a YouTube thing. It's in the Bible, Luke 1:39-45. Go ahead. I'll wait.

So, in my little version of this story, I began by saying, "Mary stepped through the door of the house and called to her cousin. 'Elizabeth, I have news!'" All of a sudden, Libby jumped in Bonnie's arms and burst forth with a cascade of bubbling laughter. Before this moment, I had heard Libby coo and squeal and sigh; but this was long and sustained laughter. Baby hysterics! Turns out my daughter was "practically perfect in every way."

When my second daughter came along two years later, I had the same concern—will she laugh? I wasn't taking any chances. We had her baptized on Christmas Day just to be safe, and it worked. Not only does Bethany laugh, she keeps us in stitches most of the time. She has a wonderful sense of humor and perfect comedic timing. So much so that I dare not let her on the stage, because once she gets hold of my audience, my career is over!

I have often said, and I sincerely believe, it is because of Christmas that we can laugh. At everything. Even death. It is the deeply spiritual significance of the season that allows such lightness of heart. All of the Christmas classics express it. For example, in his delightful short story "A Christmas Memory," Truman Capote humorously recalls his youthful excitement at the dawn of Christmas morn and its power over the death threats of others who wished to sleep late. "I tap-dance in front of closed doors. One by one the household emerges, looking as though they would like to kill...But it's Christmas, so they can't." Another example of a more sacred nature is found near the conclusion of Handel's Messiah, in which he gives us the joyous duet asking the question "O death, where is thy sting?" The chorus answers "Thanks be to God who giveth us the victory through our Lord Jesus Christ." In both of these examples we see the opposite of "grave," which can mean "serious," is "merry," which can mean "alive." The word "merry" derives from Middle and Old English and was used to describe grass and trees, things associated with the new life of spring.

It is very interesting for me to observe this happy attitude in the face of human mortality every time I perform *A Christmas Carol*. When I utter the very first line of the story, "Marley was dead: to begin with," people grin, nudge each other with knowing looks, then squirm in their seats as if they are settling in for a funny story. And so they are, because it's Christmas. That's not to say there will never again be a sad or sober moment. No, the fact of inevitable suffering and death is all too prominent in the story, but it doesn't have to terrorize us. This is what Dickens is getting at when he describes Scrooge standing on the deck of a ship far out to sea in the midst of a dark night pondering "secrets as profound as Death," only to have his dark thoughts interrupted by laughter! The scene is immediately changed to the gay and festive party in his nephew Fred's drawing room. This seems jarring until one remembers Fred lost his mother to Death, but he doesn't live in a constant state of morbid gloom. He's happily getting on with life because of Christmas. Another example is Bob Cratchit. In the midst of his grief over the loss of Tiny Tim, he dares to make a light-hearted joke as he teases his good wife in front of the children.

And she, being of equal character, takes the joke in the spirit in which it is meant.

Speaking of the death of Tiny Tim, I shall never forget the time when that poignant scene unexpectedly brought the house down with laughter at the National Storytelling Festival in Jonesborough, Tennessee. It was the biggest performance of *A Christmas Carol* in my entire career. I was scheduled for a special presentation in the largest venue on the festival grounds—The Courthouse Tent! This huge, white circus-style tent is always pitched directly behind the county courthouse, hence the name. It fills the entire half-acre parking lot and provides comfortably shaded seating in rows and rows of chairs facing a high platform stage situated against the back wall of the tent. Above the stage are huge speakers, allowing the storyteller, wearing a headset mic, to be heard loudly and clearly by all 1,500 people filling those chairs. I say loudly and clearly. That is true unless a train comes along. Just outside, above and behind the stage on the other side of the canvas wall, runs the Norfolk & Southern Railroad, a very active freight line that regularly (as in multiple times per day) sees double and triple diesel engines pulling long trains of clattering, rumbling box cars, gondolas, flat cars, tankers, and hoppers. The noise is completely overwhelming. If a train interrupts a performance, you simply stop talking and wait for the train to pass, because even the state-of-the-art sound system cannot overcome the din and racket. When a train interrupts storytellers standing on the stage, they are presented with an extra challenge, one that the audience very much looks forward to. When the performance resumes, it is not required, but it is highly expected they will somehow or other work a train into their story.

The tent was packed. Standing room only. And my performance was going extremely well. There was laughter, lots of it, in all the right places. I had moved from the introductory scene in Scrooge's countinghouse, to Jacob Marley's surprise visit in Scrooge's apartment, through his childhood and youth with the Ghost of Christmas Past, in and out of Fezziwig's dancing party, on to the Cratchit's Christmas feast and Fred's festive gathering with the Ghost of Christmas Present. I was now using all my powers of oral interpretation to steer the narrative into the dark and gloomy shadows brought on by the Ghost of Christmas Future. The audience was with me every step of the way. It was a thrilling moment. I was more than sixty minutes into a seventy-five minute piece and you could have heard a pin drop. My listeners and I were breathing in sync. Together, through the power of storytelling and imagination, with a little help from the Spirit of

Charles Dickens, we had just entered the Cratchit family home and observed the father and mother gathered together with their children before the fireplace hearth as if it were the altar of a sacred space. With deep grief and sorrow it was noted the family circle was incomplete, as a particular stool reserved for a frail and sickly child was vacant. And then...a train whistle blew. I froze. The audience froze, their eyes still fixed directly upon me. We looked at each other for another second. The train drew nearer. The clanging of the bells on the crossing gates sounded just outside the tent. The train, now much closer, blasted another long shrill signal, warning everyone of the approaching danger. Still the audience looked to me for their cue. Now the train engine was directly above and behind me, and the engineer blasted a third signal that was so loud it caused everyone to jump. I looked at my audience. Their faces were a mixture of shock and bitter disappointment. I took just a beat, and then solemnly removed my top hat as I silently mouthed the words, "Ah, poor Tiny Tim!"

That was the only time I have ever heard a roar of laughter overpower the roar of the train in the Courthouse Tent at the National Storytelling Festival.

Much they saw, and far they went, and many homes they visited, but always with a happy end. The Spirit stood beside sick beds, and they were cheerful; on foreign lands, and they were close at home; by struggling men, and they were patient in their greater hope; by poverty, and it was rich. In almshouse, hospital, and jail, in misery's every refuge, where vain man in his little brief authority had not made fast the door, and barred the Spirit out, he left his blessing, and taught Scrooge his precepts.

It was a long night, if it were only a night; but Scrooge had his doubts of this, because the Christmas Holidays appeared to be condensed into the space of time they passed together. It was strange, too, that while Scrooge remained unaltered in his outward form, the Ghost grew older, clearly older. Scrooge had observed this change, but never spoke of it, until they left a children's Twelfth Night party, when, looking at the Spirit as they stood together in an open place, he noticed that its hair was gray.

"Are spirits' lives so short?" asked Scrooge.

"My life upon this globe, is very brief," replied the Ghost. "It ends to-night."

"To-night!" cried Scrooge.

"To-night at midnight. Hark! The time is drawing near."

The chimes were ringing the three quarters past eleven at that moment.

"Forgive me if I am not justified in what I ask," said Scrooge, looking intently at the Spirit's robe, "but I see something strange, and not belonging to yourself, pro-truding from your skirts. Is it a foot or a claw!"

"It might be a claw, for the flesh there is upon it," was the Spirit's sorrowful reply. "Look here."

From the foldings of its robe, it brought two children; wretched, abject, frightful, hideous, miserable. They knelt down at its feet, and clung upon the outside of its garment.

"Oh, Man! Look here. Look, look, down here!" exclaimed the Ghost.

They were a boy and girl. Yellow, meagre, ragged, scowling, wolfish; but prostrate, too, in their humility. Where graceful youth should have filled their features out, and touched them with its freshest tints, a stale and shrivelled hand, like that of age, had pinched, and twisted them, and pulled them into shreds. Where angels might have sat enthroned, devils lurked, and glared out menacing. No change, no degradation, no perversion of humanity, in any grade, through all the mysteries of wonderful creation, has monsters half so horrible and dread.

Scrooge started back, appalled. Having them shown to him in this way, he tried to say they were fine children, but the words choked themselves, rather than be parties to a lie of such enormous magnitude.

"Spirit! are they yours?" Scrooge could say no more.

"They are Man's," said the Spirit, looking down upon them. "And they cling to me, appealing from their fathers. This boy is Ignorance. This girl is Want. Beware them both, and all of their degree, but most of all beware this boy, for on his brow I see that written which is Doom, unless the writing be erased. Deny it!" cried the Spirit, stretching out its hand towards the city. "Slander those who tell it ye! Admit it for your factious purposes, and make it worse! And bide the end!"

"Have they no refuge or resource?" cried Scrooge.

"Are there no prisons?" said the Spirit, turning on him for the last time with his own words. "Are there no workhouses?"

The bell struck twelve.

Scrooge looked about him for the Ghost, and saw it not. As the last stroke ceased to vibrate, he remembered the prediction of old Jacob Marley, and lifting up his eyes, beheld a solemn Phantom, draped and hooded, coming, like a mist along the ground, towards him.

Ignorance & Want

VISION

Oh, Man! Look here. Look, look, down here!

Charles Dickens' little Christmas story is very much like a lovely snow globe. We take it up in our hand, give it a little shake, and watch the events of life swirl around a particular subject in a particular place at a particular time: Ebenezer Scrooge, London, Christmas Eve, 1843. At first glance we think that's all there is to it, but then we notice our own reflection in the glass of the globe looking back at us. Upon closer examination, we see ourselves in Ebenezer Scrooge and realize the time and place of the story is also our own.

Just as the orb of the snow globe enlarges the scene within it, this story gives us the opportunity to take a magnifying glass to our own hearts, look inside, and realize how blind we are. Our condition is not all that different from that of Ebenezer Scrooge. He enjoys physical sight, but cannot see anything beyond the literal. In Scrooge's vision of the world there is no love, no joy, no peace. He completely misses all the things everyone else so enthusiastically sings about. We are often just like him. How many times have you said, "I know it's Christmas, but I just can't get into the spirit?" There is the diagnosis of this vision problem: These things are spiritual. Ebenezer Scrooge has plenty of money, but he is poor in spirit. How did he come to such a sad state of affairs? Well, as is the case with spiritual blindness, it was a matter of degrees.

There are the things he refuses to see. There is such poverty all around Ebenezer Scrooge, and he simply turns a blind eye. The need for physical comfort is represented in his poor clerk's desperate attempt to warm himself at his candle. Scrooge refuses to acknowledge the need for more coal and a larger fire. The need for kinship is represented in Scrooge's gregarious nephew's invitation to dinner. Scrooge is unwilling to recognize this family relation in any way. The need for society, for social reform, is represented in the portly gentlemen who stop by Scrooge's office soliciting charitable donations. Scrooge declines to even extend to them the common courtesy of civil conversation. The need for music, art, and beauty is represented by a young caroler singing through Scrooge's keyhole. He threatens physical violence. In these instances, Scrooge is willfully blind. The needs are plain enough. In fact, they all present themselves right there in Scrooge's office, just beneath his nose, so to speak. But he will not acknowledge them in any way. He shuts everything and everyone out, "solitary as an oyster."

But it's worse than that, for an oyster has no eyes and therefore it *cannot* see. Scrooge on the other hand shuts out the world because he is *unwilling* to see. If the world breaks in and forces him to look upon the needs of others, he purposefully reinterprets the vision to match his own preconceived notions. He expects to see the worst in people. Observing his clerk's determination to conduct himself cheerfully even in difficult circumstances, he pronounces him a lunatic. Upon his nephew's invitation to a sumptuous dinner with friends and family, he declares the idea to be idiocy. When presented with the plight of the poor, he implies their condition is the result of laziness. And as for music, art, and beauty, well, in threatening to strike the young caroler he makes the idea of a song sung within his hearing into a crime equal to burglary, an attempt to break in upon his life of solitude and isolation. In all of these instances, Scrooge not only refuses to see, but looks upon others with contempt. You might say his is not a blind eye, but an evil one, glaring at the rest of the world. The result of such "glaring blindness" is myopic vision. Scrooge has an eye for only one thing—money! His business occupies him constantly. And the cashboxes, keys, padlocks, ledgers, deeds, and heavy purses stacked all about him obscure everything else.

Interestingly, after Scrooge's tragic nearsightedness is made completely evident, what follows is not condemnation, but pity. The ghost of Jacob Marley, who has been present for a long time, but only recently visible to Scrooge, laments about Scrooge's sad state, then mercifully offers him a chance for a clearer vision to see many things unremembered, things unnoticed, and things unimagined.

Each ghost sent to Scrooge by Jacob Marley, whether they be from Scrooge's past, present, or future, reveals what Scrooge has always been unable to see— deep and abiding joy. The Ghost of Christmas Past helps Scrooge recall the forgotten joys of his youth: childhood, simple pleasures, young love. The Ghost of Christmas Future reveals to Scrooge what he is in danger of missing out on: the reward of a life well-lived, a legacy of joy. But it is the Ghost of Christmas Present that magnifies for Scrooge the scenes where joy is easiest to miss. In this present world, with all of its darkness and suffering, there is still love, happiness, and hope. The vision is clearest in the home of Bob Cratchit. What hard realities one might observe peering in from outside the window! Poverty is on full display. There is a noticeable lack of food, not to mention the lack of warm clothing, proper furniture, adequate space, good health, or any real hope for the promise of tomorrow. But in spite of all of this, Scrooge observes the Cratchits "looked happier yet in the bright sprinklings of the Spirit's torch." This is the genius of Charles Dickens, to concentrate not on the misery of the poor but on their joy.

When I am on my travels as a Dickens interpreter, I often find myself eating a meal at an odd or late hour. Consequently, I frequent late-night diners. My favorite establishment is Waffle House. In fact, I enjoy the atmosphere so much—the bacon and eggs, the sassy waitresses, the honky-tonk tunes on the jukebox—I pop into my hometown Waffle House occasionally even when I am not on the road. My kids go with me. They sit up on the bar stools, swiveling back and forth, relishing the same atmosphere I enjoy. We usually play Dolly Parton on the jukebox. I appreciate how the waitresses dote on my girls, making them feel extra special by calling them "sugar pie" and "honey bun."

Some people might categorize the wait staff and fry cooks at the local Waffle House as "the working poor." But that is a completely inaccurate description, because it does not take into account all the treasures these folks possess, the things that are unseen but nonetheless of great value, like a sense of humor, pride in their work, a genuine joy in serving others, not to mention the ability to do forty-eleven things all at the same time while singing along with the jukebox as Dolly chimes, "I'll be just fine and dandy. Lord, it's like a hard candy Christmas." If you don't look closely, you miss all of that and simply look upon these hard-working people with pity. But I think they should be celebrated for having a spirit that can modulate, rise above, and belt out with Dolly Parton after the key change: "I'm barely getting through tomorrow, but still I won't let sorrow bring me way down." In fact, I wrote a story about several of the people I have met at Waffle House. I hope my audience sees the people who work there, as Dickens puts it, as "fellow-passengers to the grave, and not another race of creatures bound on other journeys."

Several years ago, I decided to devote all of the proceeds from product sales during my annual tour of *A Christmas Carol* to "the working poor." My audience was very generous and I had $1000 to distribute. On Christmas Eve, I dressed up as jolly old Saint Nicholas and hopped in the car at 1:00 am. I drove over to the local Waffle House and parked behind the dumpster at the far end of the parking lot so I could make a quick getaway. With envelopes in hand, each containing $200 cash for the three waitresses and two fry cooks, I waltzed into the Waffle House and belted out a hearty "Ho! Ho! Ho!" The place was crowded with diners, and everyone turned to see Santa. One of the waitresses looked up from the counter where she was pouring coffee and started to yell "Welcome to Waffle House," but she quickly changed to "Well, what are you doing here Santa?" I very briefly explained I was on my annual round-the-world tour, and as I flew over the restaurant I saw the lights on and stopped in for a quick rest. The waitress played right along and asked me if I wanted a cup of coffee to warm me up, it being so cold in my sleigh and all. I explained there simply wasn't time as I hadn't even seen South America yet, but I was glad to see I was not the only person who had to work on Christmas. I thanked the waitress and her fellow employees for their industry, handed each of them an envelope, and turned toward the door. Everything happened in a flash, just as I had planned. One waitress was quicker than the others in opening her envelope to see what Santa had given her. As I went through the doorway, I heard her exclaim, "Oh, my goodness! There's two hundred dollars in here!" In quick fashion, the other waitresses tore into their envelopes. I fled the scene before anyone could ask questions. As I pulled out of my parking space from behind the dumpster, I looked in my rearview mirror and saw two of the waitresses running across the parking lot, waving the envelopes over their heads and yelling "Thank you, Santa!"

The day after Christmas, I went into the diner for a cup of coffee and enjoyed eavesdropping on a conversation in which a customer asked the waitress, "Did you have a good Christmas?" She responded with "There's a lot of good people in this world. The other night a man dressed as Santa Claus came in here and gave each of us two hundred dollars." She then turned to me and offered a complimentary cup of coffee, it being so cold and all. I gratefully accepted her gift without saying another word in order to remain a "secret Santa." It was much more fun to hear the story and see the sparkling joy than to receive a personal thank you.

The next time you pass by an all-hours diner in the dark of night, think of it as a snow globe lit from within. Peer through the glass. What do you see?

The Ghost of Christmas Future

STAVE FOUR

THE LAST OF THE SPIRITS

The Phantom slowly, gravely, silently, approached. When it came near him, Scrooge bent down upon his knee; for in the very air through which this Spirit moved it seemed to scatter gloom and mystery.

It was shrouded in a deep black garment, which concealed its head, its face, its form, and left nothing of it visible save one outstretched hand. But for this it would have been difficult to detach its figure from the night, and separate it from the darkness by which it was surrounded.

He felt that it was tall and stately when it came beside him, and that its mysterious presence filled him with a solemn dread. He knew no more, for the Spirit neither spoke nor moved.

"I am in the presence of the Ghost of Christmas Yet To Come?" said Scrooge.

The Spirit answered not, but pointed downward with its hand.

"You are about to show me shadows of the things that have not happened, but will happen in the time before us," Scrooge pursued. "Is that so, Spirit?"

The upper portion of the garment was contracted for an instant in its folds, as if the Spirit had inclined its head. That was the only answer he received.

Although well used to ghostly company by this time, Scrooge feared the silent shape so much that his legs trembled beneath him, and he found that he could hardly stand when he prepared to follow it. The Spirit paused a moment, as observing his condition, and giving him time to recover.

But Scrooge was all the worse for this. It thrilled him with a vague uncertain horror, to know that behind the dusky shroud there were ghostly eyes intently fixed upon him, while he, though he stretched his own to the utmost, could see nothing but a spectral hand and one great heap of black.

"Ghost of the Future!" he exclaimed, "I fear you more than any Specter I have seen. But, as I know your purpose is to do me good, and as I hope to live to be another man from what I was, I am prepared to bear you company, and do it with a thankful heart. Will you not speak to me?"

It gave him no reply. The hand was pointed straight before them.

"Lead on!" said Scrooge. "Lead on! The night is waning fast, and it is precious time to me, I know. Lead on, Spirit!"

The Phantom moved away as it had come towards him, Scrooge followed in the shadow of its dress, which bore him up, he thought, and carried him along.

They scarcely seemed to enter the city; for the city rather seemed to spring up about them, and encompass them of its own act. But there they were, in the heart of it; on 'Change, amongst the merchants; who hurried up and down, and chinked the money in their pockets, and conversed in groups, and looked at their watches, and trifled thoughtfully with their great gold seals; and so forth, as Scrooge had seen them often.

The Spirit stopped beside one little knot of business men. Observing that the hand was pointed to them, Scrooge advanced to listen to their talk.

"No," said a great fat man with a monstrous chin, "I don't know much about it, either way. I only know he's dead."

"When did he die?" inquired another.

"Last night, I believe."

"Why, what was the matter with him?" asked a third, taking a vast quantity of snuff out of a very large snuff-box. "I thought he'd never die."

"God knows," said the first, with a yawn.

"What has he done with his money?" asked a red-faced gentleman with a pendulous excrescence on the end of his nose, that shook like the gills of a turkey-cock.

"I haven't heard," said the man with the large chin, yawning again. "Left it to his Company, perhaps. He hasn't left it to me. That's all know."

This pleasantry was received with a general laugh.

"It's likely to be a very cheap funeral," said the same speaker; "for upon my life I don't know of anybody to go to it. Suppose we make up a party and volunteer?"

"I don't mind going if a lunch is provided," observed the gentleman with the excrescence on his nose. "But I must be fed, if I make one."

Another laugh.

"Well, I am the most disinterested among you, after all," said the first speaker, "for I never wear black gloves, and I never eat lunch. But I'll offer to go, if anybody else will. When I come to think of it, I'm not at all sure that I wasn't his most particular friend; for we used to stop and speak whenever we met. Bye, bye!"

Speakers and listeners strolled away, and mixed with other groups. Scrooge knew the men, and looked towards the Spirit for an explanation.

The Phantom glided on into a street. Its finger pointed to two persons meeting. Scrooge listened again, thinking that the explanation might lie here.

He knew these men, also, perfectly. They were men of business: very wealthy, and of great importance. He had made a point always of standing well in their esteem: in a business point of view, that is; strictly in a business point of view.

"How are you?" said one.

"How are you?" returned the other.

"Well!" said the first. "Old Scratch has got his own at last, hey?"

"So I am told," returned the second. "Cold, isn't it?"

"Seasonable for Christmas time. You're not a skater, I suppose?"

"No. No. Something else to think of. Good morning!"

Not another word. That was their meeting, their conversation, and their parting.

Scrooge was at first inclined to be surprised that the Spirit should attach importance to conversations apparently so trivial; but feeling assured that they must have some hidden purpose, he set himself to consider what it was likely to be. They could scarcely be supposed to have any bearing on the death of Jacob, his old partner, for that was Past, and this Ghost's province was the Future. Nor could he think of any one immediately connected with himself, to whom he could apply them. But nothing doubting that to whomsoever they applied they had some latent moral for his own improvement, he resolved to treasure up every word he heard, and everything he saw; and especially to observe the shadow of himself when it appeared. For he had an expectation that the conduct of his future self would give him the clue he missed, and would render the solution of these riddles easy.

He looked about in that very place for his own image; but another man stood in his accustomed corner, and though the clock pointed to his usual time of day for being there, he saw no likeness of himself among the multitudes that poured in through the Porch. It gave him little surprise, however; for he had been revolving in his mind a change of life, and thought and hoped he saw his new-born resolutions carried out in this.

Quiet and dark, beside him stood the Phantom, with its outstretched hand. When he roused himself from his thoughtful quest, he fancied from the turn of the hand, and its situation in reference to himself, that the Unseen Eyes were looking at him keenly. It made him shudder, and feel very cold.

They left the busy scene, and went into an obscure part of the town, where Scrooge had never penetrated before, although he recognized its situation, and its bad repute. The ways were foul and narrow; the shops and houses wretched; the people half-naked, drunken, slipshod, ugly. Alleys and archways, like so many cesspools, disgorged their offenses of smell, and dirt, and life, upon the straggling streets; and the whole quarter reeked with crime, with filth, and misery.

Far in this den of infamous resort, there was a low-browed, beetling shop, below a pent-house roof where iron, old rags, bottles, bones, and greasy offal, were bought. Upon the floor within, were piled up heaps of rusty keys, nails, chains, hinges, files, scales, weights, and refuse iron of all kinds. Secrets that few would like to scrutinize were bred and hidden in mountains of unseemly rags, masses of corrupted fat, and sepulchers of bones. Sitting in among the wares he dealt in, by a charcoal-stove, made of old bricks, was a gray-haired rascal, nearly seventy years of age; who had screened himself from the cold air without, by a frousy curtaining of miscellaneous tatters, hung upon a line; and smoked his pipe in all the luxury of calm retirement.

Scrooge and the Phantom came into the presence of this man, just as a woman with a heavy bundle slunk into the shop. But she had scarcely entered, when another woman, similarly laden, came in too; and she was closely followed by a man in faded black, who was no less startled by the sight of them, than they had been upon the recognition of each other. After a short period of blank astonishment, in which the old man with the pipe had joined them, they all three burst into a laugh.

"Let the charwoman alone to be the first!" cried she who had entered first. "Let the laundress alone to be the second; and let the undertaker's man alone to be the third. Look here, old Joe, here's a chance! If we haven't all three met here without meaning it!"

"You couldn't have met in a better place," said old Joe, removing his pipe from his mouth. "Come into the parlor. You were made free of it long ago, you know; and the other two an't strangers. Stop till I shut the door of the shop. Ah! How it skreeks! There an't such a rusty bit of metal in the place as its own hinges, I believe; and I'm sure there's no such old bones here, as mine. Ha, ha! We're all suitable to our calling, we're well matched. Come into the parlor. Come into the parlor.

The parlour was the space behind the screen of rags. The old man raked the fire together with an old stair-rod, and having trimmed his smoky lamp (for it was night), with the stem of his pipe, put it in his mouth again.

While he did this, the woman who had already spoken, threw her bundle on the floor and sat down in a flaunting manner on a stool; crossing her elbows on her knees, and looking with a bold defiance at the other two.

"What odds then! What odds, Mrs. Dilber?" said the woman. "Every person has a right to take care of themselves. He always did!"

"That's true, indeed!" said the laundress. "No man more so."

"Why, then, don't stand staring as if you was afraid, woman; who's the wiser? We're not going to pick holes in each other's coats, I suppose?"

"No, indeed!" said Mrs. Dilber and the man together. "We should hope not."

"Very well, then!" cried the woman. "That's enough. Who's the worse for the loss of a few things like these? Not a dead man, I suppose."

"No, indeed," said Mrs. Dilber, laughing.

"If he wanted to keep 'em after he was dead, a wicked old screw," pursued the woman, "why wasn't he natural in his lifetime? If he had been, he'd have had somebody to look after him when he was struck with Death, instead of lying gasping out his last there, alone by himself."

"It's the truest word that ever was spoke," said Mrs. Dilber. "It's a judgment on him."

"I wish it was a little heavier one," replied the woman: "and it should have been, you may depend upon it, if I could have laid my hands on anything else. Open that bundle, old Joe, and let me know the value of it. Speak out plain. I'm not afraid to be the first, nor afraid for them to see it. We knew pretty well that we were helping ourselves, before we met here, I believe. It's no sin. Open the bundle, Joe."

But the gallantry of her friends would not allow of this; and the man in faded black, mounting the breach first, produced *his* plunder. It was not extensive. A seal or two, a pencil-case, a pair of sleeve-buttons, and a brooch of no great value, were all. They were severally examined and appraised by old Joe, who chalked the sums he was disposed to give for each upon the wall, and added them up into a total when he found that there was nothing more to come.

"That's your account," said Joe, "and I wouldn't give another sixpence, if I was to be boiled for not doing it. Who's next?"

Mrs. Dilber was next. Sheets and towels, a little wearing apparel, two old-fashioned silver teaspoons, a pair of sugar-tongs, and a few boots. Her account was stated on the wall in the same manner.

"I always give too much to ladies. It's a weakness of mine, and that's the way I ruin myself," said old Joe. "That's your account. If you asked me for another penny, and made it an open question, I'd repent of being so liberal, and knock off half-a-crown."

"And now undo *my* bundle, Joe," said the first woman.

Joe went down on his knees for the greater convenience of opening it, and having unfastened a great many knots, dragged out a large and heavy roll of some dark stuff.

"What do you call this?" said Joe. "Bed-curtains!"

"Ah!" returned the woman, laughing and leaning forward on her crossed arms. "Bed-curtains!"

"You don't mean to say you took 'em down, rings and all, with him lying there?" said Joe.

"Yes I do," replied the woman. "Why not?"

"You were born to make your fortune," said Joe, "and you'll certainly do it."

"I certainly shan't hold my hand, when I can get anything in it by reaching it out, for the sake of such a man as He was, I promise you, Joe," returned the woman coolly. "Don't drop that oil upon the blankets, now."

"His blankets?" asked Joe.

"Whose else's do you think?" replied the woman. "He isn't likely to take cold without 'em, I dare say."

"I hope he didn't die of anything catching? Eh?" said old Joe, stopping in his work, and looking up.

"Don't you be afraid of that," returned the woman. "I an't so fond of his company that I'd loiter about him for such things, if he did. Ah! You may look through that shirt till your eyes ache; but you won't find a hole in it, nor a threadbare place. It's the best he had, and a fine one too. They'd have wasted it, if it hadn't been for me."

"What do you call wasting of it?" asked old Joe.

"Putting it on him to be buried in, to be sure," replied the woman with a laugh. "Somebody was fool enough to do it, but I took it off again. If calico an't good enough for such a purpose, it isn't good enough for anything. It's quite as becoming to the body. He can't look uglier than he did in that one."

Scrooge listened to this dialogue in horror. As they sat grouped about their spoil, in the scanty light afforded by the old man's lamp, he viewed them with a detestation and disgust, which could hardly have been greater, though they had been obscene demons, marketing the corpse itself.

"Ha, ha!" laughed the same woman, when old Joe, producing a flannel bag with money in it, told out their several gains upon the ground. "This is the end of it, you see! He frightened every one away from him when he was alive, to profit us when he was dead! Ha, ha, ha!"

"Spirit!" said Scrooge, shuddering from head to foot. "I see, I see. The case of this unhappy man might be my own. My life tends that way, now. Merciful Heaven, what is this!"

He recoiled in terror, for the scene had changed, and now he almost touched a bed: a bare, uncurtained bed: on which, beneath a ragged sheet, there lay a something covered up, which, though it was dumb, announced itself in awful language.

The room was very dark, too dark to be observed with any accuracy, though Scrooge glanced round it in obedience to a secret impulse, anxious to know what kind of room it was. A pale light, rising in the outer air, fell straight upon the bed; and on it, plundered and bereft, unwatched, unwept, uncared for, was the body of this man.

Scrooge glanced towards the Phantom. Its steady hand was pointed to the head. The cover was so carelessly adjusted that the slightest raising of it, the motion of a finger upon Scrooge's part, would have disclosed the face. He thought of it, felt how easy it would be to do, and longed to do it; but had no more power to withdraw the veil than to dismiss the specter at his side.

Oh cold, cold, rigid, dreadful Death, set up thine altar here, and dress it with such terrors as thou hast at thy command: for this is thy dominion! But of the loved, revered, and honored head, thou canst not turn one hair to thy dread purposes, or make one feature odious. It is not that the hand is heavy and will fall down when released; it is not that the heart and pulse are still; but that the hand was open, generous, and true; the heart brave, warm, and tender; and the pulse a man's. Strike, Shadow, strike! And see his good deeds springing from the wound, to sow the world with life immortal!

No voice pronounced these words in Scrooge's ears, and yet he heard them when he looked upon the bed. He thought, if this man could be raised up now, what would be his foremost thoughts? Avarice, hard dealing, griping cares? They have brought him to a rich end, truly!

He lay, in the dark empty house, with not a man, a woman, or a child, to say he was kind to me in this or that, and for the memory of one kind word I will be kind to him. A cat was tearing at the door, and there was a sound of gnawing rats beneath the hearth-stone. What *they* wanted in the room of death, and why they were so restless and disturbed, Scrooge did not dare to think.

"Spirit!" he said, "this is a fearful place. In leaving it, I shall not leave its lesson, trust me. Let us go!"

Still the Ghost pointed with an unmoved finger to the head.

"I understand you," Scrooge returned, "and I would do it, if I could. But I have not the power, Spirit. I have not the power."

Again it seemed to look upon him.

"If there is any person in the town, who feels emotion caused by this man's death," said Scrooge quite agonized, "show that person to me, Spirit, I beseech you!"

The phantom spread its dark robe before him for a moment, like a wing; and withdrawing it, revealed a room by daylight, where a mother and her children were.

She was expecting some one, and with anxious eagerness; for she walked up and down the room; started at every sound; looked out from the window; glanced at the clock; tried, but in vain, to work with her needle; and could hardly bear the voices of the children in their play.

At length the long-expected knock was heard. She hurried to the door, and met her husband; a man whose face was care-worn and depressed, though he was young. There was a remarkable expression in it now; a kind of serious delight of which he felt ashamed, and which he struggled to repress.

He sat down to the dinner that had been hoarding for him by the fire; and when she asked him faintly what news (which was not until after a long silence), he appeared embarrassed how to answer.

"Is it good," she said, "or bad?"—to help him.

"Bad," he answered.

"We are quite ruined?"

"No. There is hope yet, Caroline."

"If *he* relents," she said, amazed, "there is! Nothing is past hope, if such a miracle has happened."

"He is past relenting," said her husband. "He is dead."

She was a mild and patient creature if her face spoke truth; but she was thankful in her soul to hear it, and she said so, with clasped hands. She prayed forgiveness the next moment, and was sorry; but the first was the emotion of her heart.

"What the half-drunken woman whom I told you of last night, said to me, when I tried to see him and obtain a week's delay; and what I thought was a mere excuse to avoid me; turns out to have been quite true. He was not only very ill, but dying, then."

"To whom will our debt be transferred?"

"I don't know. But before that time we shall be ready with the money; and even though we were not, it would be bad fortune indeed to find so merciless a creditor in his successor. We may sleep to-night with light hearts, Caroline!"

Yes. Soften it as they would, their hearts were lighter. The children's faces hushed, and clustered round to hear what they so little understood, were brighter; and it was a happier house for this man's death! The only emotion that the Ghost could show him, caused by the event, was one of pleasure.

"Let me see some tenderness connected with a death," said Scrooge; "or that dark chamber, Spirit, which we left just now, will be for ever present to me."

The Ghost conducted him through several streets familiar to his feet; and as they went along, Scrooge looked here and there to find himself, but nowhere was he to be seen. They entered poor Bob Cratchit's house; the dwelling he had visited before; and found the mother and the children seated round the fire.

Quiet. Very quiet. The noisy little Cratchits were as still as statues in one corner, and sat looking up at Peter, who had a book before him. The mother and her daughters were engaged in sewing. But surely they were very quiet!

"'And He took a child, and set him in the midst of them.'"

Where had Scrooge heard those words? He had not dreamed them. The boy must have read them out, as he and the Spirit crossed the threshold. Why did he not go on?

The mother laid her work upon the table, and put her hand up to her face.

"The color hurts my eyes," she said.

The color? Ah, poor Tiny Tim!

"They're better now again," said Cratchit's wife. "It makes them weak by candle-light; and I wouldn't show weak eyes to your father when he comes home, for the world. It must be near his time."

"Past it rather," Peter answered, shutting up his book. "But I think he's walked a little slower than he used, these few last evenings, mother."

They were very quiet again. At last she said, and in a steady cheerful voice, that only faltered once:

"I have known him walk with—I have known him walk with Tiny Tim upon his shoulder, very fast indeed."

"And so have I," cried Peter. "Often."

"And so have I!" exclaimed another. So had all.

"But he was very light to carry," she resumed, intent upon her work, "and his father loved him so, that it was no trouble—no trouble. And there is your father at the door!"

She hurried out to meet him; and little Bob in his comforter—he had need of it, poor fellow—came in. His tea was ready for him on the hob, and they all tried who should help him to it most. Then the two young Cratchits got upon his knees and laid, each child a little cheek, against his face, as if they said, "Don't mind it, father. Don't be grieved!"

Bob was very cheerful with them, and spoke pleasantly to all the family. He looked at the work upon the table, and praised the industry and speed of Mrs. Cratchit and the girls. They would be done long before Sunday he said.

"Sunday! You went to-day then, Robert?" said his wife.

"Yes, my dear," returned Bob. "I wish you could have gone. It would have done you good to see how green a place it is. But you'll see it often. I promised him that I would walk there on a Sunday. My little, little child!" cried Bob. "My little child!"

He broke down all at once. He couldn't help it. If he could have helped it, he and his child would have been farther apart perhaps than they were.

He left the room, and went up stairs into the room above, which was lighted cheerfully, and hung with Christmas. There was a chair set close beside the child, and there were signs of some one having been there, lately. Poor Bob sat down in it, and when he had thought a little and composed himself, he kissed the little face. He was reconciled to what had happened, and went down again quite happy.

They drew about the fire, and talked; the girls and mother working still. Bob told them of the extraordinary kindness of Mr. Scrooge's nephew, whom he had scarcely seen but once, and who, meeting him in the street that day, and seeing that he looked a little—"just a little down you know" said Bob, enquired what had happened to distress him. "On which," said Bob, "for he is the pleasantest-spoken gentleman you ever heard, I told him. 'I am heartily sorry for it, Mr. Cratchit, he said, 'and heartily sorry for your good wife.' By the bye, how he ever knew *that*, I don't know."

"Knew what, my dear?"

"Why, that you were a good wife," replied Bob.

"Everybody knows that!" said Peter.

"Very well observed, my boy!" cried Bob. "I hope they do. 'Heartily sorry,' he said. 'for your good wife. If I can be of service to you in any way,' he said, giving me his card, 'that's where I live. Pray come to me.' Now, it wasn't," cried Bob, "for the sake of anything he might be able to do for us, so much as for his kind way, that this was quite delightful. It really seemed as if he had known our Tiny Tim, and felt with us."

"I'm sure he's a good soul!" said Mrs. Cratchit.

"You would be surer of it, my dear," returned Bob, "if you saw and spoke to him. I shouldn't be at all surprised, mark what I say, if he got Peter a better situation."

"Only hear that, Peter," said Mrs. Cratchit.

"And then," cried one of the girls, "Peter will be keeping company with some one, and setting up for himself."

"Get along with you!" retorted Peter, grinning.

"It's just as likely as not." said Bob, "one of these days; though there's plenty of time for that, my dear. But however and whenever we part from one another, I am sure we shall none of us forget poor Tiny Tim—shall we—or this first parting that there was among us?"

"Never, father!" cried they all.

"And I know," said Bob, "I know, my dears, that when we recollect how patient and how mild he was; although he was a little, little child; we shall not quarrel easily among ourselves, and forget poor Tiny Tim in doing it."

"No, never, father!" they all cried again.

"I am very happy," said little Bob, "I am very happy!"

Mrs. Cratchit kissed him, his daughters kissed him, the two young Cratchits kissed him, and Peter and himself shook hands. Spirit of Tiny Tim, thy childish essence was from God!

Specter," said Scrooge, "something informs me that our parting moment is at hand. I know it, but I know not how. Tell me what man that was whom we saw lying dead?"

The Ghost of Christmas Yet To Come conveyed him, as before—though at a different time, he thought: indeed, there seemed no order in these latter visions, save that they were in the Future—into the resorts of business men, but showed him not himself. Indeed, the Spirit did not stay for anything, but went straight on, as to the end just now desired, until besought by Scrooge to tarry for a moment.

"This court," said Scrooge, "through which we hurry now, is where my place of occupation is, and has been for a length of time. I see the house. Let me behold what I shall be, in days to come."

The Spirit stopped; the hand was pointed elsewhere.

"The house is yonder," Scrooge exclaimed. "Why do you point away?"

The inexorable finger underwent no change.

Scrooge hastened to the window of his office, and looked in. It was an office still, but not his. The furniture was not the same, and the figure in the chair was not himself. The Phantom pointed as before.

He joined it once again, and wondering why and whither he had gone, accompanied it until they reached an iron gate. He paused to look round before entering.

A churchyard. Here, then, the wretched man whose name he had now to learn, lay underneath the ground. It was a worthy place. Walled in by houses; overrun by grass and weeds, the growth of vegetation's death, not life; choked up with too much burying; fat with repleted appetite. A worthy place!

The Spirit stood among the graves, and pointed down to One. He advanced towards it trembling. The Phantom was exactly as it had been, but he dreaded that he saw new meaning in its solemn shape.

"Before I draw nearer to that stone to which you point," said Scrooge, "answer me one question. Are these the shadows of the things that Will be, or are they shadows of the things that May be, only?"

Still the Ghost pointed downward to the grave by which it stood.

"Men's courses will foreshadow certain ends, to which, if persevered in, they must lead," said Scrooge. "But if the courses be departed from, the ends will change. Say it is thus with what you show me!"

The Spirit was immovable as ever.

Scrooge crept towards it, trembling as he went; and following the finger, read upon the stone of the neglected grave his own name, Ebenezer Scrooge.

"Am *I* that man who lay upon the bed?" he cried, upon his knees.

The finger pointed from the grave to him, and back again.

"No, Spirit! Oh no, no!"

The finger still was there.

"Spirit!" he cried, tight clutching at its robe, "hear me! I am not the man I was. I will not be the man I must have been but for this intercourse. Why show me this, if I am past all hope?"

For the first time the hand appeared to shake.

"Good Spirit," he pursued, as down upon the ground he fell before it: "Your nature intercedes for me, and pities me. Assure me that I yet may change these shadows you have shown me, by an altered life!"

The kind hand trembled.

"I will honor Christmas in my heart, and try to keep it all the year. I will live in the Past, the Present, and the Future. The Spirits of all Three shall strive within me. I will not shut out the lessons that they teach. Oh, tell me I may sponge away the writing on this stone!"

In his agony, he caught the spectral hand. It sought to free itself, but he was strong in his entreaty, and detained it. The Spirit, stronger yet, repulsed him.

Holding up his hands in one last prayer to have his fate reversed, he saw an alteration in the Phantom's hood and dress. It shrunk, collapsed, and dwindled down into a bedpost.

STAVE FIVE

THE END OF IT

Yes! and the bedpost was his own. The bed was his own, the room was his own. Best and happiest of all, the Time before him was his own, to make amends in!

"I will live in the Past, the Present, and the Future!" Scrooge repeated, as he scrambled out of bed. "The Spirits of all Three shall strive within me. Oh Jacob Marley! Heaven, and the Christmas Time be praised for this! I say it on my knees, old Jacob; on my knees!"

He was so fluttered and so glowing with his good intentions, that his broken voice would scarcely answer to his call. He had been sobbing violently in his conflict with the Spirit, and his face was wet with tears.

"They are not torn down," cried Scrooge, folding one of his bed-curtains in his arms, "they are not torn down, rings and all. They are here: I am here: the shadows of the things that would have been, may be dispelled. They will be. I know they will!"

His hands were busy with his garments all this time: turning them inside out, putting them on upside down, tearing them, mislaying them, making them parties to every kind of extravagance.

"I don't know what to do!" cried Scrooge, laughing and crying in the same breath; and making a perfect Laocoön of himself with his stockings. "I am as light as a feather, I am as happy as an angel, I am as merry as a school-boy. I am as giddy as a drunken man. A merry Christmas to everybody! A happy New Year to all the world. Hallo here! Whoop! Hallo!"

He had frisked into the sitting-room, and was now standing there: perfectly winded.

"There's the saucepan that the gruel was in!" cried Scrooge, starting off again, and going round the fire-place. "There's the door, by which the Ghost of Jacob Marley entered! There's the corner where the Ghost of Christmas Present sat! There's the window where I saw the wandering Spirits! It's all right, it's all true, it all happened. Ha ha ha!"

Really, for a man who had been out of practice for so many years, it was a splendid laugh, a most illustrious laugh. The father of a long, long, line of brilliant laughs!

"I don't know what day of the month it is!" said Scrooge. "I don't know how long I've been among the Spirits. I don't know anything. I'm quite a baby. Never mind. I don't care. I'd rather be a baby. Hallo! Whoop! Hallo here!"

He was checked in his transports by the churches ringing out the lustiest peals he had ever heard. Clash, clang, hammer, ding, dong, bell. Bell, dong, ding, hammer, clang, clash! Oh, glorious, glorious!

Running to the window, he opened it, and put out his head. No fog, no mist; clear, bright, jovial, stirring, cold; cold, piping for the blood to dance to; Golden sunlight; Heavenly sky; sweet fresh air; merry bells. Oh, glorious. Glorious!

"What's to-day?" cried Scrooge, calling downward to a boy in Sunday clothes, who perhaps had loitered in to look about him.

"Eh?" returned the boy, with all his might of wonder.

"What's to-day, my fine fellow?" said Scrooge.

"To-day!" replied the boy. "Why, Christmas Day."

"It's Christmas Day!" said Scrooge to himself. "I haven't missed it. The Spirits have done it all in one night. They can do anything they like. Of course they can. Of course they can. Hallo, my fine fellow!"

"Hallo!" returned the boy.

"Do you know the Poulterer's, in the next street but one, at the corner?" Scrooge inquired.

"I should hope I did," replied the lad.

"An intelligent boy!" said Scrooge. "A remarkable boy! Do you know whether they've sold the prize Turkey that was hanging up there? Not the little prize Turkey: the big one?"

"What, the one as big as me?" returned the boy.

"What a delightful boy!" said Scrooge. "It's a pleasure to talk to him. Yes, my buck!"

"It's hanging there now," replied the boy.

"Is it?" said Scrooge. "Go and buy it."

"Walk-er!" exclaimed the boy.

"No, no," said Scrooge, "I am in earnest. Go and buy it, and tell 'em to bring it here, that I may give them the direction where to take it. Come back with the man, and I'll give you a shilling. Come back with him in less than five minutes, and I'll give you half-a-crown!"

The boy was off like a shot. He must have had a steady hand at a trigger who could have got a shot off half so fast.

"I'll send it to Bob Cratchit's!" whispered Scrooge, rubbing his hands, and splitting with a laugh. "He shan't know who sends it. It's twice the size of Tiny Tim. Joe Miller never made such a joke as sending it to Bob's will be!"

The hand in which he wrote the address was not a steady one, but write it he did, somehow, and went down stairs to open the street door, ready for the coming of the poulterer's man. As he stood there, waiting his arrival, the knocker caught his eye.

"I shall love it, as long as I live!" cried Scrooge, patting it with his hand. "I scarcely ever looked at it before. What an honest expression it has in its face! It's a wonderful knocker!—Here's the Turkey. Hallo! Whoop! How are you! Merry Christmas!"

It *was* a Turkey! He never could have stood upon his legs, that bird. He would have snapped 'em short off in a minute, like sticks of sealing-wax.

"Why, it's impossible to carry that to Camden Town," said Scrooge. "You must have a cab."

The chuckle with which he said this, and the chuckle with which he paid for the Turkey, and the chuckle with which he paid for the cab, and the chuckle with which he recompensed the boy, were only to be exceeded by the chuckle with which he sat down breathless in his chair again, and chuckled till he cried.

Shaving was not an easy task, for his hand continued to shake very much; and shaving requires attention, even when you don't dance while you are at it. But if he had cut the end of his nose off, he would have put a piece of sticking-plaister over it, and been quite satisfied.

He dressed himself "all in his best," and at last got out into the streets. The people were by this time pouring forth, as he had seen them with the Ghost of Christmas Present; and walking with his hands behind him, Scrooge regarded every one with a delighted smile. He looked so irresistibly pleasant, in a word, that three or four good-humored fellows said, "Good morning, sir! A merry Christmas to you!" And Scrooge said often afterward, that of all the blithe sounds he had ever heard, those were the blithest in his ears.

He had not gone far, when coming on towards him he beheld the portly gentleman, who had walked into his counting-house the day before and said, "Scrooge and Marley's, I believe?" It sent a pang across his heart to think how this old gentleman would look upon him when they met; but he knew what path lay straight before him, and he took it.

"My dear sir," said Scrooge, quickening his pace, and taking the old gentleman by both his hands. "How do you do? I hope you succeeded yesterday. It was very kind of you. A merry Christmas to you, sir!"

"Mr. Scrooge?"

"Yes," said Scrooge. "That is my name, and I fear it may not be pleasant to you. Allow me to ask your pardon. And will you have the goodness"—here Scrooge whispered in his ear.

"Lord bless me!" cried the gentleman, as if his breath were gone, "My dear Mr. Scrooge, are you serious?"

"If you please," said Scrooge. "Not a farthing less. A great many back-payments are included in it, I assure you. Will you do me that favor?"

"My dear sir," said the other, shaking hands with him. "I don't know what to say to such munifi—

"Don't say anything, please," retorted Scrooge. "Come and see me. Will you come and see me?"

"I will!" cried the old gentleman. And it was clear he meant to do it.

"Thank'ee," said Scrooge. "I am much obliged to you. I thank you fifty times. Bless you!"

He went to church, and walked about the streets, and watched the people hurrying to and fro, and patted children on the head, and questioned beggars, and looked down into the kitchens of houses, and up to the windows; and found that everything could yield him pleasure. He had never dreamed that any walk—that anything—could give him so much happiness. In the afternoon, he turned his steps towards his nephew's house.

He passed the door a dozen times, before he had the courage to go up and knock. But he made a dash, and did it:

"Is your master at home, my dear?" said Scrooge to the girl. Nice girl! Very.

"Yes, sir."

"Where is he, my love?" said Scrooge.

"He's in the dining-room, sir, along with mistress. I'll show you up stairs, if you please."

"Thank'ee. He knows me," said Scrooge, with his hand already on the dining-room lock. "I'll go in here, my dear."

He turned it gently, and sidled his face in, round the door. They were looking at the table (which was spread out in great array); for these young housekeepers are always nervous on such points, and like to see that everything is right.

"Fred!" said Scrooge.

Dear heart alive, how his niece by marriage started! Scrooge had forgotten, for the moment, about her sitting in the corner with the footstool, or he wouldn't have done it, on any account.

"Why bless my soul!" cried Fred, "who's that?"

"It's I. Your uncle Scrooge. I have come to dinner. Will you let me in, Fred?"

Let him in! It is a mercy he didn't shake his arm off. He was at home in five minutes. Nothing could be heartier. His niece looked just the same. So did Topper when *he* came. So did the plump sister, when *she* came. So did every one when *they* came. Wonderful party, wonderful games, wonderful unanimity, won-der-ful happiness!

But he was early at the office next morning. Oh he was early there. If he could only be there first, and catch Bob Cratchit coming late! That was the thing he had set his heart upon.

And he did it; yes he did! The clock struck nine. No Bob. A quarter past. No Bob. He was full eighteen minutes and a half, behind his time. Scrooge sat with his door wide open, that he might see him come into the Tank.

His hat was off, before he opened the door; his comforter too. He was on his stool in a jiffy; driving away with his pen, as if he were trying to overtake nine o'clock.

"Hallo!" growled Scrooge, in his accustomed voice as near as he could feign it. "What do you mean by coming here at this time of day?"

"I'm very sorry, sir," said Bob. "I *am* behind my time."

"You are?" repeated Scrooge. "Yes. I think you are. Step this way, if you please."

"It's only once a year, sir," pleaded Bob, appearing from the Tank. "It shall not be repeated. I was making rather merry yesterday, sir."

"Now, I'll tell you what, my friend," said Scrooge, "I am not going to stand this sort of thing any longer. And therefore," he continued, leaping from his stool, and giving Bob such a dig in the waistcoat that he staggered back into the Tank again: "and therefore I am about to raise your salary!"

Bob trembled, and got a little nearer to the ruler. He had a momentary idea of knocking Scrooge down with it; holding him; and calling to the people in the court for help and a strait-waistcoat.

"A merry Christmas, Bob!" said Scrooge, with an earnestness that could not be mistaken, as he clapped him on the back. "A merrier Christmas, Bob, my good fellow, than I have given you, for many a year! I'll raise your salary, and endeavor to assist your struggling family, and we will discuss your affairs this very afternoon, over a Christmas bowl of smoking bishop, Bob! Make up the fires, and buy another coal-scuttle before you dot another i, Bob Cratchit!"

Scrooge was better than his word. He did it all, and infinitely more; and to Tiny Tim, who did not die, he was a second father. He became as good a friend, as good a master, and as good a man, as the good old city knew, or any other good old city, town, or borough, in the good old world. Some people laughed to see the alteration in him, but he let them laugh, and little heeded them; for he was wise enough to know that nothing ever happened on this globe, for good, at which some people did not have their fill of laughter in the outset; and knowing that such as these would be blind anyway, he thought it quite as well that they should wrinkle up their eyes in grins, as have the malady in less attractive forms. His own heart laughed: and that was quite enough for him.

He had no further intercourse with Spirits, but lived upon the Total Abstinence Principle, ever afterwards; and it was always said of him, that he knew how to keep Christmas well, if any man alive possessed the knowledge. May that be truly said of us, and all of us! And so, as Tiny Tim observed, God Bless Us, Every One!

A Christmas Bowl of Smoking Bishop

TIME

Best and happiest of all, the Time before him was his own, to make amends in!

It is 10:14 am. Before hunching over the computer to begin writing this essay I sat at the kitchen table with my wife, enjoying a second cup of coffee and talking about everything and nothing on a lovely spring morning. The coffee was good, my favorite brand. The company was wonderful. My wife is my favorite person. And the conversation was stimulating. Topics ranged from Tudor England and the Epistle to the Hebrews to violin lessons, racial injustice, and a dramatic crime series on Amazon Prime. Oh, and cake! She told me about a cake recipe. But none of these things could be properly enjoyed without the gift of time. What a gift was given to me! On Wednesday, March 24, 2021, I was given two hours to sit, sip, and savor life.

Benjamin Franklin wrote "Dost thou love life? Then do not squander time, for that is the stuff life is made of." I imagine Charles Dickens was well aware of this quotation. He was certainly aware of the concept. In his brief little novel, which doesn't even run 200 pages and can be read in an afternoon, Dickens explores the vast subject of time—past, present, and future. It is more than a little ironic that an author known for lengthy descriptive passages, drawn out plots, and overly long stories would address such an expansive topic in such a short work.

It is said he wrote the story in a white heat of passionate fury. Dickens' personal correspondence confirms this notion. On October 24, 1843, he wrote "I plunged headlong into a little scheme… [that] will occupy every moment of my waking time, up to the Christmas Holidays." A bit later he wrote "I have been working from morning until night upon my little Christmas book; and have really had no time to think of anything but that." On November 21, 1843, he dashed off a short note to a friend saying "I am afraid I may not be in the way tomorrow; and therefore write to you. For I am finishing a little Book for Christmas, and contemplate a Bolt, to do so in peace. As soon as I have done, I will let you know. And then I hope we shall take a glass of Grog together; for I have not seen you since I was grey." *A Christmas Carol* was published on December 19, 1843. The whole story was written, edited, illustrated, and published in eight weeks time. (It's taken me over two years to write this book, and Dickens' words are more than half the manuscript. Good grief!)

Why the rush? There are several plausible theories. Perhaps Dickens needed the cash. He tended to spend money even more quickly than he could earn it. And yet, he insisted on keeping the retail price of the book low so people of modest means could afford to buy a copy. Maybe time was a limited resource, because he was also working on another project, *The Life and Adventures of Martin Chuzzlewit*. However, it was not unusual for Dickens, as is the case with most creative types, to juggle several ideas at the same time. Not to mention he was the father of ten children, which means he certainly knew how to handle many things at once! And then of course, since he was writing a holiday themed story, maybe he was simply in a hurry to get it out before the Christmas shopping season had passed. As history shows, if that was his concern, it was unfounded. The book sold well, very well, year-round.

I think the fervor had more to do with passion than any practical concern. Dickens had been mulling over this "ghost of an idea" for quite a while. His creative process involved lots of thinking time. He would regularly take hours-long strolls through the city streets late at night, observing, imagining, contemplating, and worrying over the details of his stories. In this case it seems when he got the story completely worked out in his mind, he was desperate to get it down on paper as quickly as possible. Time is a precious commodity and Dickens didn't want to waste a minute.

Dickens was desperate to deliver a very important message. Oddly enough, he was in a hurry to remind people to slow down. The Industrial Revolution was building up steam and life in Victorian England, particularly in the city of London, was now being lived at a more rapid pace than anyone had ever before experienced. Mechanization sped the processes of manufacturing and transportation, which in turn shortened the time it took to get goods to market. Demand was rising, business was booming, customers were consuming, and now more than ever, time was money!

However, progress comes with a price tag. It became all too easy to get caught up in the hurly-burly of such a rapid race, particularly where the world of business was concerned, and lose sight of the most precious things. Once those precious things were out of sight, they were out of mind, forgotten. There was nothing left but a dull, gray, daily grind. Consequently, Charles Dickens opens his story with a portrait of a man who is not alive, but merely existing. But then, we read these familiar words: "Once upon a *time*." And what a good and promising time it is too for "of all the good days of the year, on Christmas Eve"! And yet, this precious gift of time is nearly lost as old Scrooge sits busy in his countinghouse.

And there is the reason why Dickens so desperately dashes off this story in such quick fashion. He knows many a Scrooge sits on the edge of eternal loss. There is only a "nick of time" for redemption because the days are evil. Underscoring this theme, Dickens fills his little book with references to seconds, minutes, hours, days, dates, seasons, clocks, calendars, and all sorts of ways to mark the past, the present, and the future.

It is interesting to note that even though the story is divided into three distinct sections—past, present, and future—we spend more time with the Ghost of Christmas Present than any other phantom. Dickens is saying it is only in the present, in the time we have today, this hour, this minute, that we can effectively make a difference for ourselves and others. The past cannot be altered. The future is unclear. The present is everything.

We speak of this idea as "being present." This was very much a trademark of Charles Dickens' personality. He tended to devote himself completely to the task before him, particularly where the writing of this little Christmas story was concerned. And what was the result? A classic story that annually reminds us during the season in which we see the ending of one year and the beginning of another to stop, consider, and be "happy, grateful, pleased with one another, and contented with the time" afforded to us. For this is the only way, in as much as is possible for mortal man, to redeem the past and secure the future.

Several years ago I was hired by an art museum to present *A Christmas Carol* as a compliment to an exhibit on the life and times of Charles Dickens. The director and I had a meeting to figure out details for my show and concluded visitors to the museum would be in too much of a hurry to sit and listen to a ninety-minute retelling of this classic tale. What they needed was just a quick, little snippet of the story. So, we decided I would be set up in a corner of one of the galleries with a small group of chairs. As museum visitors wandered through, I would greet them, invite them to choose their favorite part of the old, familiar story, and sit down for just ten to fifteen minutes as I told that brief section, like a movie clip. Or should I say "Dickens at a clip"? This was our plan. But when the day came for me to be on hand for the droves of visitors who were sure to crowd the museum to see Storyteller Tim Lowry perform for ten minutes, nobody came. I stood around talking to the museum director for a long time and she assured me the lack of an audience was no reflection on the quality of my work. People were just busy. It being the Christmas holiday shopping season and all, it was hard for families to find the time. Finally, two patrons walked in.

My good friends Jim and Delores Sitterson had read about the Dickens exhibit and my performance in the newspaper, and here they were to take it all in. I explained our plan and invited them to choose their favorite section of *A Christmas Carol.*

Delores, a southern lady who is never in a hurry, said, "Well Tim, if we are only going to get to hear a brief section of the story, we better hear the ending. I would just hate to leave without Scrooge having the chance to get his heart right."

My friends took their seats and I launched into the final stave of the story, beginning with the words "Best and happiest of all [for Ebenezer Scrooge], the Time before him was his own, to make amends in! 'I will live in the Past, the Present, and the Future!' Scrooge repeated, as he scrambled out of bed." Ten minutes later, I concluded with "God Bless Us, Every One!" I received an enthusiastic round of applause from my audience of two. Jim and Delores thanked me for the little bit of the story. We chatted about family news and such, then they wandered off to see the rest of the exhibit.

After a while, they came back and Delores said, "Tim, Jim and I have been talking and we hate to leave without hearing the part about Scrooge in the graveyard. After all, it is a ghost story and it seems a shame not to hear the really scary and creepy part."

Since there was no one else there to object, I agreed. They sat back down and I began. "The clock struck twelve. As the last stroke of midnight ceased to vibrate Scrooge lifted up his eyes and beheld a Phantom, hooded and draped, moving like a mist across the ground towards him."

After I concluded, Jim and Delores just sat there for several seconds. Finally, Delores said, "Thank you."

Then they went away again…only to return.

Delores said, "Tim, Jim and I were talking. That graveyard scene is so dark and gloomy. It being Christmas and all, we shouldn't leave things there. How about telling us the part about the Ghost of Christmas Present and the Cratchits and all of that. Let's hear a merry part."

I dutifully obliged ending with the Ghost saying "Midnight! Hark, the time is drawing near!"

Delores clapped her hands together, obviously pleased. Jim nodded his approval. They went away. They came back.

"Tim, Jim and I have been talking." (I wondered about the truth of this statement as I had yet to hear Jim say a word.) "We've heard about the Ghosts of Christmases Future and Present. They say things come in threes. It just doesn't seem wise to leave without hearing about the Ghost of Christmas Past."

I began with "Scrooge awoke and listened for chiming of the predicted hour." And a few minutes later I concluded with the ghost's disappearance as it exclaimed, "My time grows short!"

Delores said, "Hmm."

Jim looked contemplative, and after several minutes he finally said, "We might as well hear how it starts."

And without any further prompting I began to quote "Marley was dead: to begin with...."

Jim and Delores spent the whole afternoon with me and we enjoyed *A Christmas Carol* together—backwards! It was one of the strangest and yet most delightful afternoons I have ever spent. While the rest of the world was busy with so many other things, I sat in a beautiful art gallery decorated for the season with dear friends I had not seen in years, enjoying the whole of Dickens' *A Christmas Carol.* Unhurried, un-rushed, uninterrupted.

Writer Walter Wangerin, Jr. once said Christmas is an intrusion, a divine disruption of our busy, self-absorbed, mundane existence. I believe that to be true. And like any divine disruption, it is shocking and wonderful at the same time. It is a much-needed thing, Christmas. Otherwise we would stumble blindly forward with nothing in our vision but the immediate, thinking of what we must do, where we must go, who we must talk to, what things must be accomplished, how we are going to get it all done...like so many Scrooges worried only about ourselves. Then the Spirit of Christmases Past, Present, and Future breaks in upon us. The One who Was, and Is, and Is To Come jolts us out of self-absorption and into reverential awe. We are once again reminded of what is truly important, where our focus should be, the true nature of our existence, and the great lack of gratitude on our part. So we pause on Christmas to remember, to meditate, to consider the reason for all of the bustle and hurry, the meaning of our business. And in the quiet moment, when we once again have a clear view of the blessed hope that is Christmas we leap up and shout with all the other people of the Earth, "God Bless Us, Every One!"

BIBLIOGRAPHY

Ackroyd, Peter. *The Life and Times of Charles Dickens.* New York: Hydra Publishing, 2002.

Andrews, Evan. "Why Do We Kiss Under the Mistletoe?" History, December 13, 2021. https://www.history. com/news/why-do-we-kiss-under-the-mistletoe.

Capote, Truman. *Breakfast at Tiffany's, A Short Novel and Three Stories.* New York: Random House, 1958.

Chesterton, G. K. *Charles Dickens, The Last of the Great Men.* New York: The Readers Club, 1942.

Clark, Gertrude. "St Dunstan: The saint who put horse-shoes on the devil's hooves." Catholic Herald, May 19, 2020. https://catholicherald.co.uk/st-dunstan-the-saint-who-put-horseshoes-on-the-devils-hooves/.

Dickens, Cedric. *Christmas With Dickens.* Arlington, VA: The Belvedere Press, 1993. Dickens, Cedric. *Dining With Dickens.* Goring-on-Thames, England: Elvendon Press, 1984.

Dickens, Charles. *A Christmas Carol* (illustrated by Arthur Rackham). London: William Heinemann, 1948.

Dickens, Charles. *Christmas Tales by Charles Dickens* (illustrated by H. M. Brock). New York: Gallery Books, 1990.

Dickens, Charles. *Speeches: Literary and Social.* London: Chatto and Windus, 1880.

Dickens, Charles. "Where We Stopped Growing." *Household Words.* London: Bradbury and Evans, January 1, 1853.

Dickens, Charles, and Clement Clarke Moore. *An Arthur Rackham Christmas: A Christmas Carol and The Night Before Christmas.* Mineola, NY: Calla Editions, 2013.

Donner, Clive, director. *A Christmas Carol.* Entertainment Partners Ltd, December 17, 1984. DVD.

Ellis, Elizabeth. *Prepare to Scare.* Marion, MI: Parkhurst Brothers Publishers, Inc., 2021.

Forster, John. *The Life of Charles Dickens, The Illustrated Edition.* New York: Sterling Signature, 2011.

Franklin, Benjamin. *Poor Richard's Almanack.* Mt. Vernon, NY: Peter Pauper Press, 1980.

Frazer, James. *The Golden Bough: A Study in Magic and Religion.* New York: The Macmillan Company, 1935.

Gottlieb, Robert. *Great Expectations: The Sons and Daughters of Charles Dickens.* New York: Farrar, Straus and Giroux, 2012.

Graves, Robert. *The White Goddess: A Historical Grammar of Poetic Myth.* London: Faber and Faber Limited, 1961.

Hatton, Joseph. *Reminiscences of J. L. Toole, Third Edition.* London: Hurst and Blackett, 1889.

Hearn, Michael Patrick (Editor). *The Annotated Christmas Carol.* New York: W. W. Norton & Company, 2004.

Henson, Brian director. *The Muppet Christmas Carol.* Walt Disney Pictures & Jim Henson Productions, December 11, 1992. DVD.

Henson, Jim. "Danny Boy." YouTube. January 2, 2007. https://www.youtube.com/watch?v=OCbuRA_D3KU.

Josephson, Matthew. *Edison: A Biography.* New York: McGraw-Hill, 1959.

Kaplan, Fred. *Dickens: A Biography.* New York: William Morrow & Company, 1988.

Levitow, Abe, director. *Mister Magoo's Christmas Carol.* United Productions of America, December 18, 1962. DVD.

Lewis, C. S. *The Lion, the Witch, and the Wardrobe.* New York: Harper Collins Publishers, 2000.

London, Jack. "To Build a Fire." Story of the Week. February 25, 2011. http://storyoftheweek.loa. org/2011/02/to-build-fire.html.

Manning, Mick, Brita Granstrom. *Charles Dickens: Scenes From An Extraordinary Life*. London: Frances Lincoln Children's Books, 2011.

Marsden, Robert S. (Chairman). "God Rest You Merry, Gentlemen." *Trinity Hymnal*. Philadelphia: Orthodox Presbyterian Church, 1961.

Mattinson, Burney, director. *Mickey's Christmas Carol*. Walt Disney Animation Studios, December 16, 1983. DVD.

"Merry." *Online Etymology Dictionary*. 2001. https://www. etymonline.com/search?q=merry.

Parton, Dolly. "Hard Candy Christmas." Track 7 on *Once Upon A Christmas*. Sony Music Entertainment, 1984, Spotify. https://open.spotify.com/ track/0uTVChzibEWKrXojPaJ9y1.

Pentreath, Rosie. "The Surprising Origin of Christmas Carols: Explained." Classic FM. December 23, 2021. https://www.classicfm.com/discover-music/ occasions/christmas/carol-history-origins/.

Pool, Daniel. *What Jane Austen Ate and Charles Dickens Knew*. New York: Simon & Schuster, 1993.

Relph, Ingeborg, Penny Stanway. *Christmas, A Cook's Tour*. Oxford: Lion Publishing, 1991.

Saint Ignatious of Loyola. *The Spiritual Exercises of St. Ignatious* (translated by Anthony Mottola). New York: Image Books, 2014.

Saint John of the Cross. *The Dark Night of the Soul* (translated by David Lewis). London: T. Baker, 1908.

Stevenson, Robert, director. *Mary Poppins.* Walt Disney Pictures, 1964. https://www.youtube.com/watch?v=yNHRXNvFmZ8.

Händel, Georg Friedrich. *Messiah.* Robert Shaw, Conductor. Atlanta Symphony Orchestra and Atlanta Symphony Orchestra Chamber Chorus. Telarc Records, 1984. CD.

The Spectator. "Anonymous review of Dickens' *A Christmas Carol.*" London: December 23, 1843.

Wangerin, Walter. *Preparing for Jesus.* Grand Rapids, MI: Zondervan Publishing House, 1999.

Watts, Alan S. *The Life and Times of Charles Dickens.* New York: Crescent Books, 1991.

Welch, Bob. *52 Little Lessons from A Christmas Carol.* Nashville, TN: Nelson Books, 2015.

Zemeckis, Robert, Director. *A Christmas Carol.* Walt Disney Pictures, November 6, 2009. DVD.

Made in the USA
Columbia, SC
17 September 2024

41983142R00137